Dedicated To The Memory Of

JOHN PEPKA

(1913 - 1977)

Most of what you predicted has
tragically come to pass.
I no longer wonder how you knew.
Now the world will see if your solution
will work as well as you thought it could.
Rest in peace Dad. You certainly earned it.
And my eternal love as well.

Democracy For Americans

Democracy For Americans

It is now self evident that
five hundred and forty-five Federal lawmakers
cannot do the thinking for
two hundred and sixty million Americans.

The problem with Democracy
is that it's never been tried.

The Author

Democracy For Americans

TABLE
OF CONTENTS

Can the Blind Lead The Blind?

Christianity And Democracy

Employment

Cultural Relativism

Accountability

Power

MESSAGES

WHAT IS TO BE DONE?

When Land Meant A Kingdom And Hope Was A Dragon

by

Vincent Mountjoy-Pepka

From A Dream

"Watch your head, sir!" Commander Jake Gorman shouted above the roar of the squall. The President was nearly shoved through the back passenger door of the black limousine by his bodyguards. The heavy door slipped from Gorman's fingers and was slammed shut by a wet blast of wind. Rain pounded everything as the squall ripped at the Secret Service Agents' overcoats. Gorman plunged into the front passenger seat as the remaining agents pried open doors on other cars before diving in.

Gorman wiped the water from his face and then from his headset phone with a towel handed to him by the driver. He spoke deadpan from years of habit into his microphone, "Everybody on board? O.K. The motorcade is to proceed with no deviation from planned parade route. There's no air escort. The helicopters can't get up. Stay alert. It's fifteen hours twenty one minutes." He switched off his transmitter and said to the driver, "Let's roll, Tommy."

In spite of the foul weather, the Commander's pleasure was plain on his face. Now that Air Force One had finally landed, and he had the Chief in the car, Gorman only wanted one thing: To get the President to the Capitol building on time for the State of the Union address. As soon as he was deposited, Grant Fisher, the senior officer of the Service, would take charge and Gorman could go home.

The Commander already knew the state of the Union. He wasn't going to listen to the broadcast. It could be summed up in one word. Disaster. The depression was so bad that only the President still called it recession. Via the video monitor in the dash board, Gorman could see the worried look on the President's face as he spoke to the Secretary of State sitting beside him.

"I wouldn't want to be in Vee Dub's shoes tonight," Tommy muttered.   The two separate compartments were exclusively soundproof.

"No," was all Gorman said quietly.   'Vee Dub' didn't refer to the famous German car but was the Secret Service code word for this President, his initials being "V" and "W". The handle was a natural also due to the chief executive's amply rounded body just like the car.

Tommy continued, "Everybody's calling him that now, his aides, even the press when they aren't calling him *V*ery-*W*ide or worse. His approval rating is the lowest ever recorded." The weather had unnerved Tommy and he could see little through the hosing the windshield was getting.

Gorman declared, "That's enough. Just get us there." A year ago, the Commander would have reprimanded the driver for the remark.

"I'm trying. You see what it's like outside."

Gorman wasn't thinking about the foul weather. A hurricane was stalled-out more or less harmlessly at sea one hundred miles east of Annapolis.   Yet it was managing to whirl the clouds over Washington D.C. into a fine fury.

"Do you think Vee Dub will talk about the comet?" Tommy asked nervously as they moved out. The astronomers of the world were agog over a newly discovered comet. The comet's head and tail were now visible even in daylight but only where it wasn't raining. It was due for its closest fly-by of earth in ten days.

"I've no idea." Nor do I care, Gorman thought. Like most Americans these days, he was taking his portion of happiness in interpersonal pleasures. He knew his job was secure no matter what happened to the rest of the economy. "Tonight, I'm seeing my daughter for the first time in two years. She's brought my new grandson by train. Little Jake...I've never seen him."

"Where do they live?"

"Phoenix. They should be at my home by now. I can't wait!"

In spite of the downpour, with the on-board imaging radar, the motorcade moved rapidly along the beltway. Exactly on schedule the President was deposited safely inside the Capital Dome.

"Vee Dub, please try and hold steady," Renee pleaded gently as, with brush and pot in hand, he struggled to finish applying the President's makeup. The Chief Executive obediently sat perfectly still as the paint was applied to his face.

Outside the small temporary enclosure, built just for him and only for this night, was another door through which he would soon make his entrance. It was a short walk, measured in numbers of feet, to the speaker's podium in the House of Representative's chamber, although tonight the distance felt like miles. He suddenly remembered being here last year and wished he had the last twelve months to live over again. If only he could have foreseen the future.

As was the custom, both Houses of Congress were present. All nine members of the Supreme Court, the Joint Chiefs, the Cabinet and Vice President and of course the News Media were in attendance. Additionally, the gallery was packed with high-rollers meaning the top of the heap of lobbyists, political action committee members and those with special interests plus other hangers on with 'access'. The Americans, whose interests were theoretically being served by this lot, were waiting at home in front of their televisions but only the bravest among them. Each was hoping to hear a different message.

"This morning the Post suggested that I, the President of the United State of America, the Vice President and my entire Cabinet resign. At least there was one laugh in today's paper if at my expense." The Washington D.C. newspaper had been the first to declare that this administration was under a 'state of siege' due to the economy, personal scandals and lack of honor.

"Well, that's just awful," Renee declared in a non-committal tone. He was concentrating on his task at hand.

"I've told myself it doesn't matter. Actually it makes things just that much more interesting." Finding his attempt at lightheartedness lost on Renee, the President tried again to concentrate on his speech.

Practicing out loud, he said, "The new investment package I'm recommending, if passed by Congress, will create a million new federal jobs over the next eighteen months. That the marginal income tax rate will have to be raised another six percent on top of the four percent from last year is a small concession."

It bothered the Chief Executive not at all that a government study had disclosed that for every Civil Service job created through raising taxes three jobs in the private productive sector would be lost. One job in the military cost five. One scientist to make weapons of mass destruction cost ten. All irrelevant facts serving only to cloud the political issues.

He, the President of the United States of America would declare that, "Americans need to get to work again. It is up to this government to show the way by bold and innovative action!"

Renee stepped out of the enclosure to retrieve a fresh can of hair spray. The President's heart sank in his chest and he shuddered involuntarily. He wondered for a terrifying moment, if he could even open his mouth publicly to utter the words he'd rehearsed.

In sudden desperation, he put a hand to his forehead and quietly prayed to whatever force might be listening, "Please rescue me from this mess. I'll do anything." But just as quickly he reminded himself that this way of thinking was weak and cowardly for a man. If only he could hope that there was really a way out of the quicksand. "If only I can get re-elected, I'd have four more years to prove I've been right all along."

Renee returned and saw the President's hand covering his forehead. "Oh, no! I'll just have to do it again. Please, Vee Dub, remember not to touch your face when you are on television. Especially not your nose."

The President obediently sat at attention once again. He was thinking that Americans needed ten million new jobs, not one million. Nevertheless, the political issues were clear. He would repeat what he had proclaimed all year. Out loud he continued to practice, "The rich business community isn't cooperating with my policies by creating new jobs in the private sector. Of course, the recession is Wall Street's fault. New higher business tax rates, surtaxes, health insurance taxes and value added taxes will prove to them that this administration is serious about prospering Americans. They must pay their fair share. The Republican leaders in the House and Senate must stop wrangling over partisan issues and start cooperating!" They had successfully blocked his plan to eliminate all personal tax deductions across the board.

No deductions would have meant no loopholes and therefore no cheats, not to mention more tax revenues. Not that he'd ever expected them to cooperate. They did however provide the all important whipping post for his own failures.

Nor were the United We Stand renegades of any use. Their facts about the government were accurate but irrelevant. Tonight, he would appeal to their patriotism and ask them to stop dividing the nation and support him. But he knew it wouldn't be enough because, and he had to admit, not even his own Party leaders wanted to publicly stand with him anymore.

Except for the rank and file of Federal employees and his wife, who would tonight stand bravely at his side, the President was alone politically and he knew it. The increased taxes on Social Security recipients had alienated the seniors. Last year's two hundred sixty billion dollar income tax increase had K.O.'d the economy which had alienated just about every one else. The general election was only a year and a half away. This new package had to work if he was to have any chance at all of reversing the polls and winning re-election.

Economic facts were irrelevant. Political reality was all that mattered. The formula for re-election was tried and true. Party control of the government depended upon ever expanding government jobs and welfare benefits which insured loyal voters. It was axiomatic. Or had been up until now.

The President shuddered inwardly as a chilling thought gripped him. A trillion dollars didn't buy the kind of votes that it used to when he was younger. What would his hero's FDR, JFK or LBJ think of him?

The signal came from the woman technician in charge of the television cameras. Ripley Haerden, the First Lady or 'co-President' as she preferred to be called, entered the enclosure. She said, "Vee Dub--it's time. Thank you, Renee," she added for the makeup man, dismissing him.

After Renee had gone the President said, "You look beautiful tonight, Ripley."

"And you are handsome," she responded as she reached for him taking his hands in her own. She could see the worry in his face.

"Better not kiss me. Renee would have a fit."

"Well...then break a leg," Ripley said, kissing him anyway.

The President and the First Lady made their way out to the podium amid perfunctory applause from the Democrat's side of the room. He had just begun to address his audience when it started.

At first it was a low level rumbling like the sound of an overloaded truck passing nearby. The rumbling was followed within moments by a horrible shudder from the floor.

The room began to rock back and forth as the lights flickered once, then twice before going out, plunging them into utter darkness. People could be heard screaming above the dislocating noise which followed. There was one final grinding belch before they were all swallowed by inky silence.

The comet's deep space orbit around the sun brought it closer to the earth than even the most alarmist scientist had first predicted. While there was yet no projected danger of collision, its gaseous cloud and vapor trail reflected the sun's light illuminated the sky at night and intensified the normal light of day. Just short of three weeks passed and the American people still had nothing tangible, except for the freak second hurricane vortex, to explain the cataclysmic disaster. The second vortex had materialized and just as mysteriously dematerialized in the sky over Washington that night. Nevertheless the disappearance of the Capitol building with their leaders was linked in every American's mind to the massive comet. All that remained was the hole in the ground. There was no trace as not even the concrete foundation was spared. It was as if it had been yanked out of the ground and carried off. But by whom and to where no one knew. The only possible explanation was too frightening to consider.

Jake Gorman had witnessed the event or as much of it as he could see through the rain as he had left for home that night. At least he thought he had. He could have sworn that, just for a moment, he saw what looked like a gigantic winged dragon descend from the vortex and attach its enormous claws to the dome. The next morning Gorman had been found unconscious with a gash on his head in the park across the plaza on the wet grass next to a fallen tree.

After repeating the story several times for the attending physicians and psychoanalysts at the hospital they decided the vision must have been an hallucination induced by the injury to Gorman's head from the scattering debris.

The American people themselves, once they got over the initial shock of the cataclysm wasted no time in taking action.

Except for its massive size, the comet was identical to all the others known to earth scientists. And after the fact, they produced evidence that the comet returned   once every thousand years including records from a Chinese astronomer, other ancient star gazers, and cave drawings.

It was composed of nothing more than rocks and ice. As it approached the sun, the surface melted, forming an atmosphere which was in turn blown off to form the tail. The closer the comet came to the sun the more intense the heat, the more gas was created, and thus the bigger the tail grew.

For two and a half weeks the Capitol building had sat securely on the very nose of the comet, a part that always faced the sun. It was held in place by the comet's own slight pull of gravity and the still stronger forward motion of the heavenly object. At its present distance from the sun, the melting ice billowed forth a warm breathable atmosphere. The President, Congress, Supreme Court members, government leaders, joint chiefs, the lobbyists and the news media quite literally lived on a world of their own.

They were all quite safe. By 'safe', I mean that they were physically well and uninjured, if one can be 'safe' living on the nose of a comet hurtling toward the sun. Not one of them had died although at first some thought they would die of fright. But with the emergency food stores in the basement of the Dome, they were not wanting for sustenance. At least not yet. After the initial panic and shock the leaders found brave and prolific words for one another.

The only continuous warmth, light and water were found outside of the building on the surface itself. There was a magnificent view of the earth and most of the thousand people congregated in a large open area. Under direct order from the President, the Joint Chiefs had declared with somewhat giddy certainty that the situation at home was well in hand: Those in the Pentagon would know exactly what had happened. In short order NASA's entire space shuttle fleet would be commandeered for a massive and unprecedented rescue. Surely the Russian Republic would volunteer its resources to the same end. Any other scenario was unthinkable. Whether it was true or not was beside the point. The President had a political duty to keep moral as high as possible.

For hours upon days the various leaders and political factions had taken turns making brave speeches for one another's benefit. But as days counted by into weeks the earth seemed to approach, growing ever larger then passed and got slightly smaller as they moved further away.

It had today passed completely from sight below the short horizon. Even to the most deluded among them it was becoming painfully obvious that not only was a speedy rescue not forthcoming but would soon be impossible to mount.

Their collective fears and despair erupted as several in the United We Stand faction broke with the tacit pretense and accused the President and the Joint Chiefs of bungling. They insisted that the whole crisis was caused by the government's lack of preparation. They had squandered the citizens' money instead of spending it wisely.

The Republicans joined in the verbal hammering of both the President and the Democrats by proclaiming this would not have happened under either George Bush or Ronald Reagan. Surely the crises would have been anticipated and forestalled had a Republican with military experience been the Commander in Chief instead of a Democrat anti-war protestor.

The Democrats in both Houses reciprocated instinctively. The Speaker attacked the twelve years of Reagan and Bush. Republican squandering of resources on adventures in other countries and deficit spending were responsible for the lack of domestic preparativeness. The damage done by those two was too great to be undone by the current administration.

The anchors of the major television news networks followed by reading a joint declaration: Each network had covered the issues in depth. In their studied and objective opinions all three political Parties, but especially both Branches of Congress and the Executive were equally to blame. Furthermore if it weren't for the domination of the government by the special interests, lobbyists and political action committees, the budget would have been balanced and there would have been a surplus to spend on preparatory measures.

Ripley retorted that the newscasters were in fact nothing more than highly paid hemorrhoid cream salesmen. She exclaimed furiously that the news was deliberately slanted negatively to sell the products like hemorrhoid cream and extra strength aspirins to get rid of the pains caused by watching the manufactured news aimed against her brilliant health care plan.

The expert witnesses, as they are known when giving testimony but known to the rest of the world as lobbyists, PACs and Special Interests, were called next. It wasn't their fault, they said, that government was corrupt. All they did was take advantage of the greed of the politicians. To them it was simply business. Supply and demand.

Next the Blacks blamed the racist Whites and were accused of racism themselves. The women's coalition blamed male domination as the root cause but got nothing except derisive laughter from one of the Congressmen. The distraction lasted until one women planted an melting ice boulder on his head.

The Gay Rights spokesperson blamed the homophobes in Congress and the Supreme Court. The so-called voices of the poor blamed the greed of middle class and rich and were in turn blamed for causing their own constituents' problems.

The Women's Choice faction blamed the Right-to-Life delegates. The Right-to-Lifers spat out that everyone but their own group was morally bankrupt. 'Murderers all bound for hell!'

No one it seemed, even at this latest of all possible dates, understood, much less appreciated the complexities of others' rights and needs for redress. At this everyone started shouting angry words.

The President persuaded them all to be quiet for a moment. He explained that if only the Congress and Media had agreed to and carried out his agenda, somehow, some way, none of this would have happened. Somehow they wouldn't all be trapped on the edge of this comet hurtling toward the sun. If only they had passed his investment program the first time he asked everything would have been fine. "You still just don't get it!" He exclaimed bitterly at the end.

After a stunned pause, the Republican Whip shook his fist at the President as he exclaimed, "You canceled the Space Defence program! We could have blasted the comet rather than let it get so close to earth! You've murdered us!"

Someone yelled, 'Kill him!' The mass of people, by this time delirious, took up the murderous chant. Hundreds surged for the President and his wife, Ripley. At this the Chief Justice of the Supreme Court emerged from cowering in the Dome with a bull horn. Above the shouting, he screeched that he was ordering Grant Fisher of the Secret Service to put an end to the debate. That's when the brawl started in earnest.

The fist fighting, punching, biting, gouging and stone throwing continued for a long time as the battle spilled out over the wet rocks and away from the Dome. By now each one of them realized that their lives would end here on this rock.

They had nothing to sustain them any more except an all-consuming hate for one another. Initially the Democrats and their PACs had the upper hand since they were present in superior numbers to any other single group. But it soon became apparent that some individuals among them were beating members of their own group just as viciously as they pummelled the enemy.

Grant Fisher and his small group of Secret Service agents did their best to protect the President, his wife and the Vice President but they were vastly outnumbered. They could do nothing but use their own bodies to shield their charges from the incoming stones. The deep reservoirs of a lifetime of hate poured out unabated. Before long many lay strewn about some with bloody noses and superficial gashes. But only those tiny few with martial arts training had inflicted serious injury. Career politicians, mostly old men armed with nothing but words, made for pathetic warriors.

At first no one noticed the dark spot circling overhead. It gradually became bigger and still bigger until its shadow covered the entire battlefield. An enormous red dragon circled flapping its wings effortlessly above their heads. It laughed and breathed fire in joyful bursts as it nodded its head in vigorous agreement with the havoc. Slowly the fighting stopped as combatants became aware of the impossibility hanging overhead. A few of the combatants had been knocked down unconscious but most were awake and terrifyingly aware of what they beheld. After the fighting stopped the dragon landed and lay prone facing the protagonists between them and the opening to the Dome.

"It's wonderful to see with my own eyes that after a thousand years you haven't changed a bit!" the dragon exclaimed howling with laughter until tears of joy rolled down its long ugly snout. "It's always this way when I return. Humans do so love to slaughter one another. But it's a pity you came unarmed. Personally, I miss the swords, especially the spiked bludgeons. But sharp stones are vastly underrated, don't you agree?" it added eagerly as if this were helpful information.

The dragon settled itself a bit, then breathed a happy sigh of relief. It said, "But now you're mine. Your whole world is mine and one day I'll incinerate your entire pitiful race. I'm just waiting for there to be enough of you maggots to make it amusing. But today, I'll take great pleasure in just toasting all of you." At this the dragon again howled with laughter and rolled over onto its back. It gleefully belched fire for miles into the atmosphere just to show off as it reveled in the joy of moment before flipping back to an upright position.

"Do any of you have anything to say before you die?" the Dragon asked with perfunctory curiosity. Not that it cared what the humans thought but after a thousand years of waiting the monster could prolong the moment of pleasure to see what they might say. "Speak up now or I won't be able to hear you," the dragon urged gently. "Don't be bashful."

The Chief Justice shook violently as he put the bull horn into the President's hands. Others, including his body guards, began pushing the reluctant leader, clothes torn and bloodied, toward the dragon. After several moments, the President found his voice and frightfully asked, "Did you bring us here?"

"Of course," the dragon responded calmly. "Who did you think? Carl Sagan?" At his own attempt at cleverness the dragon roared again, obviously enjoying its every word.

"Why?" the President persisted when the dragon finished laughing.

"Why? You can ask me why? You yourself asked for my help the very day I brought you here. Moments before your annual speech to your so-called nation. Don't you remember?"

"No. I've never, ever thought of you!" he exclaimed with petrified certainty.

"I am the 'hope' you asked for. I've always listened to your prayers most attentively. But I would have brought you here anyway. That goes for each and every one of you. You've all summoned my help often enough in the past. By the way, you can put down the bull horn. I can actually hear you quite easily."

"I don't understand," the human answered, his voice tiny and quivering. Blood ran from a gash in his forehead. He wondered where he found the courage to speak.

"I don't see why not," the dragon answered smugly. "I am, after all, the ruler of your world. It belongs to me." The dragon's answer was met with nothing more than stupefied looks. It added, "I discerned long ago that you had no protection. None of you do. It's as simple as that."

"Protection?"

"It's all in your oldest history books."

"What books? What--" groped the President but was cut off by the dragon.

"Don't tell me you haven't read about me?" the dragon asked coyly as if it'd heard this all before which in fact it had. Jumping up onto its hind legs the dragon raised its fat body and long neck and head proudly as it wagged its spiked tail banging it viciously against the Dome. It blew smoke from flared nostrils into their faces and thundered, "I am the Red Dragon! The Prince of Darkness! The Destroyer!"

"Whooo...whaaa?" he asked in terrified befuddlement.

"I--am--Satan!" it exulted. At this the dragon belched fire directly over their heads for what seemed like an eternity, scorching but not killing them. It thundered, "As a people and a nation you have rejected the one person who might have saved you. I cannot say His name aloud. But you worms, you could have. Now it's too late! Ha, Ha, Ha, Ha!" The dragon slowly fell over onto its back again as it clutched at its quivering stomach in ecstasy.

Embolden by sheer terror, the President gabbled, "You're talking about the Messiah? That's all just make believe--I didn't really understand--I tried to believe but--If I'd known--Our scientists said there was no--I didn't know--"

Belly up with its head upside down flat on the ground the dragon stopped laughing and calmly declared, "Liar! I know your thoughts. All of them. Scientists, bah! What you're trying to say is that you didn't believe in God and you didn't believe in me either. Is that it?"

"Yes," he confessed.

"Save your breath. Only human vanity and self deceit could believe in a universe that sprang into existence out of sub-atomic particles of nothing," the dragon said contemptuously. "Idiots! Everything was created. Even me! Nothing begets nothing. I know all about this generation's high tech version of why I don't fit into your lifestyle." It sneered in contempt at the word, 'lifestyle'.

"How?"

"As it so happens, I told it to you. I can make my voice sound like anything. Even your own thoughts."

"You?"

"Who else? I admit it is a challenge coming up with fresh contemporary ideas so humans of each generation will deny what is so patently obvious," admitted the dragon marvelling at his own accomplishment.

"No...this just can't be happening," the President moaned as he looked down and covered his face with one hand.

"Oh, yes." The dragon paused as if it had almost forgotten something then added, "Now, before I terminate your existence, tell the others about your dream."

"What dream?"

"You know the one. The only one you've ever had in your miserable life that matters.

He knew instantly exactly which dream the dragon was talking about. The President had been running from the memory for years. "I can't. I just can't! Please don't--"

"Tell the others, and I will spare your life. I'll even take you back to earth. But only you," the dragon laughed, reveling in the human's anguish.

There was no escape. The human could not look at the others as he began sputtering his recollection of the dream. "I--I dreamt that a black blot was growing up out of the ground at my feet."

"Louder! They can't hear you."

"The blot was alive. It was made of individual fibers. Getting larger by the moment. It grew into a flowing blanket, one fiber at a time. It got bigger and bigger until it almost covered me. I knew that once it covered me I would suffocate," the President said as he began shaking uncontrollably. He wanted desperately to live even if it meant that the rest of them had to die.

"Continue," commanded the dragon calmly.

The human's voice croaked as he obeyed, "I had a sword and tried to beat it back. For hours it seems I fought until it was just a blot again. I was exhausted. With the last remaining strength in my arms I stooped over and picked it up. It was evil brought to life. The blot was vibrating in my hand--ready to spring back and smother me again. I knew that it would. I was powerless."

"Tell them about the fibers."

"Each fiber was a lie that I had told. Or a wrong that I had done."

"Sin. The word is sin."

"Yes. My sins."

"You admit your own guilt?"

"Yes. Anything, just don't kill me. Please," he begged pathetically.

"You fashioned your own death shroud. One strand at a time. Tell them what happened next because I cannot."

This part of his dream was the most difficult to retell but the President obeyed. "I felt I'd collapse, but just then I heard a voice behind me say, 'Give it to me.' I turned, and there was Jesus Christ hanging on a cross. He said, 'Give it to me.' I had no choice. If I wanted to live I had to give the blot to him. I did it. I knew..." he sobbed as he choked out the words, "I knew then that Jesus had...had died for me. Christ died for my sins!" he gasped for air then fell to his knees then into the fetal position, covered his face with his hands and wept bitterly.

The dragon declared quietly, "You knew. As did all the rest of you. I know the thoughts of each and every one of you. You've all learned exactly the same thing that this maggot, your chosen leader, just confessed. At one time or another in your otherwise pathetic lives you rejected That which created you. You were offered the ultimate gift. You turned away. You choose to ignore what you had learned. The Great 'I Am' judges nations just as individuals are judged.   I know because I myself once lead millions--an armada if you will--powerful beings just as myself--as I once was. Yes, I was also judged. I was once so magnificent to behold that no mortal being could see my image and live! But that was in another time and in what you would call another reality. Your nation has rejected God because of your collective action and poor leadership. As a group, you lead the nation away from God. Several of you as individuals might have escaped condemnation but are nonetheless found lacking because as leaders you are judged by a higher standard. You will be punished most severely. Since you worshiped yourselves instead of Him you have no protection. It's too late to say your prayers!"

At once the dragon launched itself into the air. It circled the thousand people in one last victory barrel roll flyby celebration. The monster savored the moment flapping its enormous wings and breathing fire above their heads to instill the perfect balance of terror and desperation. It raged, "Four thousand years ago I persuaded the Pharaoh of Egypt to order all the newborn male Hebrew babies slaughtered. I tried to kill Moses before he could be used to deliver the Children of Israel from slavery. I failed! Two thousand years ago I tried this same trick with King Herod of Judea to kill the Son of God. I failed! But this time apparently I didn't fail! Your presence here proves I've won at last! It was I who told you, the lawmakers to legalize abortion. It was I who used you to slaughter thirty million of your own children. It must have worked this time--it must have! I must have succeeded in killing God's prophet for this generation! I've finally defeated God in battle! I've won a victory at last!" it gushed with hell's own fury.

A groan went up among the people.

"Time to say goodbye," it said directly to the President.

"But you said you'd spare me if I told them about my dream!" he wailed pathetically.

"I lied!" the dragon exclaimed with exultation, then added, "What did you expect? You lied all your life and as leader of the nation you honored liars. You all told so many lies until not even one among you of you could distinguish truth from fiction. You became what you beheld. You have earned me. I am the Father of all lies. Your evil desires lead you to sin. Your sin has brought you to death. Brought you to me, for I am Death!"

The dragon grinned with insane pleasure as it made what it had decided would be the last turn before the kill. "After I toast you just a bit, I am going to eat you all alive!"

At that moment high above there was a disturbance. The sight of whatever it was caused the dragon to utter horrible sounds. The flying red colossus abruptly crashed to the surface shaking everything.

The dragon awkwardly righted itself and gazed up. Focusing its attention on the new apparition which itself had grown to enormous proportions, the dragon stood on its hind legs and belched fire as it shook its massive wings defiantly at the approaching object.

The humans saw the wings of a new creature and deduced that another dragon, perhaps a rival had arrived. But as it came closer they could see what the dragon must have recognized all along: It wasn't another dragon but a magnificent eagle, even larger than the red dragon! Light shone out of it's body from the inside. The newcomer was as majestically beautiful in appearance as the dragon was horrifyingly ugly. It had the form and appearance of a bald eagle but it also seemed to be made of nothing less than congealed light.

The dragon was furious. Apparently the light of the eagle hurt the dragon's eyes and it began to stagger back, wagging its head back and forth to avoid the brilliance. The eagle effortlessly hovered directly over the Dome without touching it.

"No! No!" the dragon howled. "They are mine and mine alone! It is written! They chose this fate! They belong only to me now!"

As the humans witnessed agog, the eagle metamorphosed into a beautiful woman with skin and hair and clothes made of light. Her magnificent wings became two feathers also of light, one for each hand. She had a crown of twelve stars on her head and the moon rested under her feet.

The transformation complete, the women spoke directly to the dragon in a voice like a thousand angelic singers but as intimate as a whisper, "Holy, holy, holy is the Lord God Almighty, who was, and is and is to come."

"What do you want with me?" the dragon screeched in anguished defiance.

"I have come for these, my children," she said gesturing one arm at the humans.

The dragon, who by now couldn't stand to even look at the women, covered its face with one wing. It bellowed, "It's too late! I have waited another thousand years. They have been judged as persons and as a nation. It is my time again. It is written."

She answered, "No. They have changed. As a Nation, they have just repented. They have returned to the Great 'I Am'. Therefore, the Lord God Almighty has also listened to the prayers of these individuals." To the humans she commanded, "Enter the Dome." They sprang up as one, this time helping one another to the opening.

"When?" demanded the dragon desperate to know. "When did they return?"

"It happened in a moment of time. While you were savoring your victory and licking your lips the Nation accepted the voice of God's prophet. They repented and the Nation was redeemed."

"No! I won't allow it. I possess them! I will eat them now!" it wailed and staggered for the retreating thousand with its eyes closed and mouth wide open.

The women looked at the dragon and simply whispered, "No." And as she did the light coming out of her intensified until she was brighter than many suns. The dragon collapsed again in a heap as it screamed in anguish and rocked to bury its face. Her radiance was killing it. She whispered, "You may return to this rock after we've departed. And as it is written you may return again to earth a thousand years hence."

Her light returned to the previous level. The people had by this time found safety inside the building. The dragon lay gasping on its side. The women's arms changed back into eagle's wings and her legs into eagle's legs. With her talons she grasped the Dome and effortlessly carried the entire building aloft. Moaning, the dragon rose and then, instead of fire, it spewed forth water like a river, trying to overtake the woman and sweep her away with the torrent. As she flew across the heavens back to earth, the dragon gave chase. The earth helped the woman by opening its mouth to form a vortex and swallowed the river the dragon spewed out of its mouth. The dragon raged impotently at the woman.

Finally admitting it was powerless against her, the red monster gave up the chase. Instead the dragon went off to make preparations for the next battle against the rest of her children--those who obey God's commandment and who hold to the testimony of Jesus Christ. The women changed completely back into the form of the bald eagle as she carried her prize the final distance. But the dragon, instead of going back to the comet, landed on Earth to make preparations for the next battle. It stood on the shore of the sea to wait for the Beast.

Jake Gorman was listening to instructions on his headset. It was just before dawn. The voice on the other end reported the National Weather Center had only seen a freak vortex like this once before, exactly twenty days ago when the Capitol building disappeared. The pattern had reappeared again in exactly the same location, over Washington D.C. directly above where the Capitol building had been. Gorman was first from the Service to arrive on the scene. By coincidence he stood on the exact spot where they had found him unconscious that day three weeks ago. But now he was awake, though rubbing his eyes with disbelief.

The Capitol building had been returned to its original location, apparently completely intact. He called headquarters again on his radio and recommended they contact the Army to have the area surrounded as they had after the original disappearance.

Shining his flashlight ahead, Gorman cautiously walked out of the park, across the street and up to the Dome. In direct disobedience of orders, he wasn't waiting for reinforcements. He was astonished by his own total lack of fear. He would be the first to unravel the mystery even if it cost him his life.

A door under the colonnades slowly opened. Out into the light stepped President Van Winkle, his wife and a few of the other missing leaders. With disbelief and astonishment reflected in his voice, Gorman gushed, "Vee Dub! It is you! Are you all right, sir? Are the rest in there?"

A dazed Van Winkle recognized Gorman's voice and face. Gratitude cracked Van Winkle's expression as he looked around taking in the familiar Washington scene. At length something snapped in place in his mind. He whispered, "We made it. We're back. We all made it," ending with a sigh.

"What happened? Where--" Gorman demanded but was cut short.

"I can't even begin to give you an answer, Commander. Just get my limousine. Take me back to the White House," Van Winkle begged wearily.

At that moment the Speaker of the House emerged through the door with Grant Fisher, the head officer of the Service. Gorman said to Van Winkle, "I'm sorry sir. I don't know how to put this..." He noticed that they each had cuts needing medical attention including Van Winkle and his wife. Their clothes were torn and smelled like smoke and their hair was singed. "Let me get you to the hospital first. I'm sure the doctors--"

"No. I'm going to the situation room at the White House! I want a nuclear strike launched against that thing--that damn red monster!" Van Winkle exclaimed now alive with fury as his eyes bugged out.

"Sir?" Gorman asked incredulous. Pulling firmly on Van Winkle's arm, the Commander said, "I'll take you to the hospital myself. You can't go to the White House just yet. My car is over--"

Fisher overheard the conversation and demanded, "Gorman, why can't we go to the situation room? Answer me and that's an order!"

Addressing Van Winkle directly instead of Fisher, Gorman explained, "I'm sorry to have to be the one to tell you, sir. But you're no longer the President of the United States."

The news took a few moments to sink in but then it seemed to come as a relief to Van Winkle. He said calmly, "I see. Yes. You thought we were dead. Yes, I understand. But the Vice President and the Speaker of the House were with me. The issue of succession is spelled out in the amendments to the Constitution. I--"

"Not any more. I really think you need to talk to--"

"What do you mean?" the Speaker exclaimed interrupting the conversation. "Only Congress has the power--"

"Not any more, I'm afraid." Gorman's words left them all speechless. By now the exchange had attracted dozens of the survivors who were staggering from the Dome into the rising daybreak. The Commander took a deep breath as he decided to give them the facts with both barrels, "You see, while you were gone we...there have been some changes. The citizens have formed a new government."

"Anarchy! We were only gone twenty days!" the Speaker exclaimed for all of them.

"Yes. But once it became clear what was needed it only took a short time to call a special election to effect the changes. It's not anarchy. Far from it."

"What changes--exactly?" Van Winkle demanded.

"Are you sure you wouldn't rather have this explained to you by someone else? You must be--"

"No," Ripley Haerden declared as she re-emerged from the crowd and grabbed Gorman's arm. "I demand you explain!"

Reluctantly, Gorman continued, "You hit on it yourself. We have a Democracy now--instead of a Republic that is. As I said, the idea was so simple and made so much sense that once it was proposed, all we had to do was amend the Constitution.

"But that would have taken years!" the Speaker exclaimed in profound distress and indignant disbelief, then quickly added, "Not twenty days!"

"It was a Constitutional Convention. Over television. Every voter was invited as a delegate. We had a special national election. Democracy was voted for almost unanimously. It went fast. And it was so simple."

"Impossible! Impossible! Impossible!" The Speaker repeated as he hysterically exclaimed the word over and over. They all watched as his mouth and lips continued to move but no more sounds came out until he bent over to retch.

"Unbelievable!" Fisher whispered disgustedly at the sight and in appreciation of their whole situation.

Gorman said, "Believe it." He thought to himself without rancor that once these politicians were out of the way unable to obstruct real progress it had been easy to fix the government. Twenty days had been more than enough time. "Anyway, the citizens are sovereign over the three branches of government now. The majority gets to approve or disapprove every law, every tax, every ruling, item by item. And I do mean everything," Gorman said lowering his voice to emphasis the last phrase. After a pause to let the information sink in he added matter of fact, "We voters also have power of national referendum."

Someone asked, "What about Congress?"

"We thought you were dead. There are new Senators and Congressmen from each State. Most were appointed. But now they live and work in their home Districts and States instead of here. The White house is the temporary Capitol. The President is the only Federal office holder who lives in D.C. But he lives in Blair House." Blair House is an apartment across the street from the White House.

"Just who is President?" Van Winkle demanded to know. Gorman said the name and identified him as a former Vice President and one of the main proponents of the change from Republic to Democracy. "That lunatic? He's just a right wing Christian extremist!" Van Winkle observed sharply before he cut himself off. He almost choked on his last words as he suddenly remembered the dragon and the eagle and what he himself had said and done and what had almost happened.

Gorman was about to tell them not to worry about the new President. He wanted to tell them about how the Nation had come together in prayer and reconciliation because of the crisis. He also wanted to tell them about his daughter's extraordinary visit and her staggering knowledge of Jesus which had persuaded him to become Christian himself. He wanted to tell them about all the amazing wonders that had happened in their absence when a woman's voice pleaded from the crowd, "But what about us? After all we've been through! Are we still citizens?"

"Of course. We all have the same vote. Everybody does. You're not excluded just because you weren't here. Although we did have State funerals for you," Gorman explained and then thought aloud, "But I suppose a judge will have to declare you all legally undead for the records."

Van Winkle asked, "Can I run for election?"

"In eighteen months. Every four years just like always. Nothing has changed there. Sooner if the President is recalled by the voters in the next election."

"Recalled?"

"The voters are sovereign--a 'no confidence' vote."

"What? Well, that's something at least. And it wouldn't be the first time a dead person won an election," Van Winkle declared still not understanding but laughed uproariously at his own joke. The relief he felt at being away from the dragon was overtaking him.

The mood in the crowd lightened up considerably as most of them joined in the blissful release that only laughter brings.

As he felt his forehead, Van Winkle exclaimed, "You're right, Jake. Take us to the hospital." He then slapped the Commander's back affectionately as the crowd broke up. "It's great to be alive isn't it? How much room have you got in your car?"

By now it was getting light and thousands of people were running up and down the park lawns and across the street into the Dome. Sirens were blowing and emergency lights were every where. There was more than enough yelling and blasts from bull horns.

Uniformed police and military commandoes appeared surrounding the entire building, trying to keep the crowds away. There was so much confused activity that Gorman, Van Winkle and Ripley were largely ignored as they walked across the park to the Commander's car.

It was unusually warm for a Washington D.C. February morning. As the sun light broke over the buildings, the trio climbed into the car and shut the doors. Gorman called headquarters to report on his progress and let them know where he was headed and with whom.

As they were pulling away from the curb, Van Winkle thought aloud, "What will I do until then? Until the next election, I mean?" he asked of Ripley, then gabbled on nervously without waiting for her response, "You know we spent almost everything getting elected. And honestly, before all this happened, I didn't think I could get reelected. Now, I don't think I would even want to try. The nation's problems are just too big. And...I'll never get over what's happened to us. Much less be able to explain it. Now that we're back it just feels like a long nightmare." He paused at last as, for the first time, he noticed the pop-eyed look on his wife's dirty face. Van Winkle quickly surmised Ripley must be in shock.

Ripley's mouth moved and her voice was controlled but her eyes stared straight ahead unblinking as she suggested, "Don't decide anything now, Vee Dub," She paused for a giddy thought that was forming in her mind then abruptly declared, "You could make a fortune as a lobbyist! Every door would be open to an ex-president. Just think of the millions we could make. After the way we've been treated, we deserve it!"

Gorman flashed his Secret Service badge to the traffic officer to get past a busy intersection. Unaware of Ripley's altered state of mind Gorman interjected, "Ah, yes...well. Before you consider it, you should know it's now a capital crime for an elected official or member of his family to accept money or gifts for any reason from any lobbyist, political action committee or any special interest group. They must make their appeal directly to the voters. The same law applies to anyone who's ever held office."

The door to that option having been slammed in his face, Van Winkle demanded, "Under the new rules do I get a pension?"

"I don't know. What I do know is that whatever the Congress passes and the President signs must then be approved item by item by a majority of voters in the next general election. Every three months."

"Suppose the voters don't approve it?" Ripley asked icily, completely aware again and outraged at the very idea.

"The voters are sovereign now," Gorman tried to change the subject to another topic, "We have prayer in public schools now for those who want it."

"Just tell me how we'll earn a living?" she demanded to know.

"What about the Supreme Court ruling separating Church and State?" Van Winkle bleated. He was rapidly loosing his ability to cope with both the revelations and Ripley.

Gorman wondered if his passengers would ever comprehend as he tried again, "The voters collective will is now Constitutional by definition. It's axiomatic. In a National Democracy the government's laws or rulings, including the Supreme Court's, are subject to the vote of approval of the majority. The three branches can only advise the citizens. Exactly the opposite of the old Federal Republic." His orders were to drop them off at the hospital into the care of other Agents and return to the Dome to lend what ever assistance was needed there.

The Commander tried again to change the subject, "Have you ever had a job--a real one I mean?" Gorman asked glibly before thinking of the implications of such a question. There was silence as they turned into the hospital entrance.

"My whole life has been politics," Van Winkle answered his voice sounding more lost than defiant. "I was only gone twenty days," he mouthed pathetically. "Twenty days."

Gorman brought the car to a halt and jumped out to open the door for his ex-Chief. Van Winkle stepped out of the car then turned to give Ripley a hand. The Commander just had to say something about what had happened to him over the past twenty days. It was now or never so he plunged ahead, "Sir, if it means anything to you, the agent force has just been cut by half. I'm out myself in thirty days--but my point is, I'm Christian now and I'm just not afraid of the future any more, and you don't have to be either. It's a long story but, you see my daughter explained to me who Jesus Christ really is. God is alive! I'm filled with new Life!" he exclaimed happily then continued, "I've just made plans to start a private security company in Phoenix. My daughter lives there. And well, sir--we need legal council for the company. If you would consider--" Gorman stopped himself short when he saw the appalled look on Van Winkle's face. The agent whispered, "I understand."

"Twenty days!" Van Winkle declared then slammed the door in anger.

"God bless you, sir," Gorman said sincerely.

With Ripley in arm, Van Winkle marched through the glass doors of the hospital just as a gang of Secret Service agents, doctors and reporters mobbed them both. Gorman got behind the wheel of his car and drove away. And although he often prayed for his ex-Chief, he never looked back.

> *And I saw an angel coming down*
> *out of heaven, having the key to*
> *Hades and holding a great chain.*
> *The angel seized the dragon, that ancient*
> *serpent, who is the devil, or Satan, and*
> *bound it for a thousand years. The angel*
> *threw it into the Abyss, and locked*
> *the gate, to keep it from deceiving*
> *the nations anymore until the thousand*
> *years were ended. After that, the dragon*
> *must be set free again for a short time.*

> *From Revelation 20*

AUTHOR'S NOTES

I was not trained as a writer. I've never had a writing class. I started writing on my own in 1987 during a period of reoccurring physical disability. I'm still partially disabled.

In drafting and structuring this book, I accepted that the average reader might turn first to the chapter containing the current affair issue most important to them. If you do read this book from cover to cover you will notice that some of my ideas developed in the introduction are repeated throughout the text. I believe that the understanding and acceptance of a few basic concepts is essential to resolving a very large number of political, social and economic problems. It was therefore essential that these basic ideas be very briefly reexamined within the context of the issues.

As a young person, I was trained by my father in our very small family manufacturing business and later in college in the analytical disciplines of business, accounting, economics, finance, math. In addition, I studied political science and history. Upon graduation from college in 1975, I worked as an intern on a joint federal, state and local government project both as an evaluator and a planner of crime control projects (sponsored by the Department of Justice).

Since 1977, I have worked as a Registered Representative of several well-known national financial services corporations and recently as a investment advisory salesperson. As you will discover, I am Christian as I proudly proclaim. Over a period of fifteen years, I also trained part-time as a peer-counselor. Washington State has been my home for thirty-four of my forty-one years. In 1977 I married my childhood sweetheart. She is also my tireless editor. We have three wonderful children.

INTRODUCTION

"We need a new government."

John Pepka

This is a book of conclusions about common sense. It is also a guide to a vision. I offer herein my own political, economic and spiritual evaluation of the State of our Nation. My singular and overwhelming conclusion is that we as Americans need to amend our Constitution and peacefully change our form of government from a Federal Republic to a National Democracy. This book is above all else an invitation for you to join me and like-minded Americans in the pursuit of Democracy.

We need a new form of government if we and our progeny are to become what we must be to survive both as individuals and as a Nation. We must do this and very soon if we are to preserve any part of what we collectively value as a people.

The authors of the Declaration of Independence offered their conclusions and very little in the way of facts. Rather they offered brief summaries. They had what Thomas Paine called 'Common Sense'. Common Sense is today generally ridiculed by those in power and by those in the bureaucracy which the politicians created to support them. I have concluded that those of us who possess it, who still represent the vast majority in this country, have been dealt out of the game, especially during the political reshuffling of the last thirty years.

Because this book is about conclusions, I do not offer many facts. Like the Founders of our Nation, I'm not trying to prove anything. In Washington D.C., I have noticed as perhaps you have also, that facts don't account for much with our leaders when it comes to making decisions. No rational person could defend our present government's actions or policies.

But even if this presentation were a thousand pages or ten times that number it would still be extremely short if my goal was to chronicle all the pertinent facts pointing to what I'm advocating. The conclusions I've drawn are self-evident.

Facts are the basis for intelligent decision making. I refer to a few excellent sources in this book. But if I had included reams of facts, what would have been the point? Or more accurately the result? It would have only served the anti-Democracy forces in their ongoing war of disinformation to refute what is already painfully obvious to every adult American.

One only has to read a daily newspaper to witness the political and economic atrocity of the day brought on by the five hundred and forty-five lawmakers who govern us from Washington D.C.

The signers of the Declaration of Independence proclaimed their conclusions based upon the obvious facts of their situation known to them all. They saw the way out of the trap they were in and somehow summoned the courage to act. We must do the same but in a very different way than how Bill Clinton, Thomas Foley, Ronald Reagan or Ross Perot want us to. We have to look to ourselves.

I believe, as did the Founding Fathers, that the time for more study has passed. Now is the time for us to act together. The only question is, what action to take? This book spells out the first steps we must take to solve the real problems of our Nation.

There is a purely American common sense expression that goes like this, "If you want something done right, do it yourself." After you have finished this book you will also know the way out and be able to help yourself. What is more to the point, is that once the United States of America is a National Democracy and the citizens are sovereign, Americans will together, and for the first time, create solutions far more eloquent than I could offer on my own, based upon your own understanding of the facts. You the citizens will at last have the final say over what becomes the law of the Land.

This book was not written for the current five hundred and forty-five lawmakers who rule our country (Congress, President and Supreme Court) but for we the people of the United States, the other two hundred sixty millions who are the Nation and who are suffering on account of the aforementioned lawmaker's inability to think for us. My only message for the lawmakers is: Wake up!

Americans will realize upon reading this book that the only real problem with Democracy is that it's never been tried.

Introduction

In 1768, Samuel Adams became the first American political leader to publicly deny the authority of the King of England and his Parliament's sovereignty over the thirteen Colonies. He declared that American independence was his long range goal. On July 4, 1776 in Philadelphia, Pennsylvania, fifty-six men signed a declaration which contained, among others, the words in the paragraph below. In doing so they officially set in motion a revolution which gave birth to a completely new form of government. They created the United States of America, a Federal Republic. With its three branches of government, Executive, Legislative and Judicial, it became the model for dozens of other nation states freeing themselves from Monarchical and Colonial domination.

Those fifty-six men proclaimed that it was self-evident that all men are created equal. Men were endowed by their Creator with absolute rights, that could not be taken away by any government, what ever its form and regardless of whatever claim that government had to sovereignty. The citizens themselves had the right and the duty to institute new governments whenever such rights were violated. Such authority was not given by governments but by God.

"We hold these Truths to be self-evident, that all Men are created equal, that they are endowed by their Creator with certain unalienable Rights, that among these are Life, Liberty, and the Pursuit of Happiness-- That to secure these Rights, Governments are instituted among Men, deriving their just Powers from the Consent of the Governed, that whenever any Form of Government becomes destructive of these Ends, it is the Right of the People to alter or abolish it, and to institute new Government, laying its Foundation on such Principles, and organizing its Powers in such Form, as to them shall seem most likely to effect their Safety and Happiness. Prudence, indeed, will dictate that Governments long established should not be changed for light and transient Causes; and accordingly all Experience hath shewn, that Mankind are more disposed to suffer, while Evils are sufferable, than to right themselves by abolishing the Forms to which they are accustomed. But when a long Train of Abuses and Usurpations, pursuing invariable the same Object to reduce them under absolute Despotism, it is their Right, it is their Duty, to throw off such Government, and to provide new Guards for their future Security."

From the Declaration of Independence
signed July 4, 1776.

The notion of equality as being self-evident and God-given was considered dangerous and treasonous by the monarchies and those whose fortunes and positions in society depended upon the continuation of the status quo. It was 'The' revolutionary concept in a world ruled by kings, emperors, tsars and their tiny numbers of peers. To the peers, it was obvious that only kings had this 'divine' right to rule albeit through official ministers.

To them, elected members of Parliament in England were one thing. But the Colonies were, after all, merely property, so they reasoned. Colonists were subjects of the Crown. That's the way it had always been. Anyone who disagreed deserved death.

To prove it, the King of England's ministers sent troops and war ships to North America intending to put a final end to the traitors and their ilk. But the Treaty of Paris, signed in 1783, and formally ending the bloody eight year war which followed the signing of the Declaration of Independence, left the Americans victorious and their self-evident truths wholly vindicated.

The Founding Fathers, as they were respectfully referred to when I was a child, wanted above all a Democracy. They talked and wrote about it incessantly, risking everything as many died to bring the new government to life. The concept dominated their lives until they died. But they hadn't the technical means to implement their ideal. They never realized their dream.

The Federal Republic which we now have is a compromise. It is a Nation ruled by five hundred and forty-five lawmakers most of whom are lawyers. It is not a Democracy wherein every person has an equal vote, but a Republic where citizens are theoretically represented by an elite few. It has evolved over two centuries, but it is imperative to your understanding that you realize the Republic itself was originally just a compromise.

The founders of our Republic could imagine a Democracy but hadn't the means to engage it. More than any other factor they lacked the technology to bring all the citizens together at one time to vote on each piece of legislation. Our form of government, with its three branches, (Legislative, Executive and Judicial) and its unnecessarily complicated system of electing lawmakers was never anything more than a temporary solution.

On the East coast of North American in 1776, the mass of English-speaking European descendents lived in a primitive agricultural or frontier society. By 1790 the U.S. population was only three million nine hundred thousand inhabitants. The physical center of the population was twenty-three miles east of Baltimore, Md. Cities were tiny compared to those of today and had relatively no infrastructure.

Transportation between the original States was by horseback, or on wooden seagoing sailing ships. Overland, it could take months to travel from the northern states to the south of the country. There were few roads outside the cities.

In cities, the rare places where the mud streets were 'paved', bricks and raw planks of wood were used. There was no electricity and therefore no telephone or telegraph. There were no internal combustion or steam engines, no trains, no automobiles and no airplanes. Modern means of communication such as television, radio, satellites, computers, etc., most of which we take for granted, hadn't even been thought of, much less invented.

The Founder's compromise was to have a representative government based upon the ideals of Democracy. They did the best they could with what resources they had. Considering that they had to simultaneously raise an army of mostly farmers and woodsmen to fight the professional army and navy of England, arguably the most powerful nation of that period, what they accomplished is nothing less than miraculous.

But today we do have the means to effect a National Democracy. We can all assemble to vote on every issue item by item. The means are television, telephone and computers. You and I and all others like us who believe in Democracy can make the dream come true. We can and should peacefully change the Federal Republic to a National Democracy. The reasons are obvious and multitudinous. We don't need to compromise any longer. The wisdom of the majority, those with common sense, must prevail.

Just as the Founders believed that control over the Army and Navy was too important to be left in the hands of the military, I believe it is likewise self-evident today that the laws of our nation are too important to be left solely in the hands of the lawyers who are ruling over us.

Under Democracy, the wisdom of the majority as expressed in ballots would rule. The citizens would be directly sovereign over the three branches of government (Executive, Legislative and Judicial) unlike now under the Republic where <u>they</u> are sovereign over <u>us</u>. Each citizen through their vote would have the same power as every other citizen. I know that this concept gratifies some and frightens others. The immediate effect of Democracy, under my proposal, would be that for the first time the citizens of the United States, in general elections, would approve or disapprove, item by item, every law and tax passed by the Legislature and signed by the President before its provisions are either carried out or canceled.

The citizens would vote to approve or disapprove every Supreme Court ruling on matters of constitutional or unconstitutionality. Unlike now, under Democracy, the citizens would also have the right of National Referendum. The citizens would have the right to confirm or reject declarations of war, approve or reject all treaties, approve or reject impeachment decisions and would have the direct power to elect or recall any Federal official including members of the Supreme Court for any reason at the will of the majority of the voters in any general election. In essence, you the citizen would be sovereign for the very first time.

Federal office holders, whether they are Republican, or Democrat or Independent, and those who work for them in the Legislative, Executive and Judicial Branches of the United States government, have lost sight of the fact that America is a place where people live. It's now a cliche that Abraham Lincoln's plea at Gettysburg that, "...government of the people, by the people, for the people, shall not perish for the earth," has been replaced by, "...government of the politicians, by the special interests, for the foreign lobbyists, shall not fail to deliver all the wealth." It's enough to make a grown man weep.

Democrats are federal republicans just as Republicans and the United We Stand America, Inc. followers of Ross Perot are federal republicans. Personally, I'm dismayed by the numbers, especially of young men and women, I meet who don't know that our government is a Republic and not a Democracy. But they're not totally to blame. They are the products of the last thirty years of Federally dictated public education. It is also worth pointing out that most of the so-called democracies in the world are, in fact, republics, patterned after the United States. The elected members of the two major parties and the wannabes of United We Stand America, Inc. know that their power can only exist as it is today in a Republic. I predict that the majority of them will not want the Republic to end because their power will evaporate once Democracy is established.

Introduction

There is a movement within our Nation to vilify Americans who call attention to self-evident truths. The reasons they do this are complex and I discuss many of them in this book. But as an introduction, in addition to the self-evident truths listed in the Declaration of Independence, the Constitution and Bill of Rights, it's worth a review of at least of few of the other self-evident truths:

On December 18, 1865 it became self-evident under the law of the United States that human beings could not own other human beings. The Thirteenth Amendment abolished slavery and involuntary servitude except as punishment for a crime.

Only July 28, 1868, it became self-evident under the Fourteenth Amendment that citizenship rights granted under the Constitution could not be abridged. Due process must be granted to every citizen.

On March 30, 1870 it became self-evident under the Fifteenth Amendment that the right to vote could not be denied because of race.

On August 26, 1920 it became self-evident under the Nineteenth Amendment that women had the unalienable right to vote.

In 1954, the Supreme Court ruled that it was apparent that state-sanctioned segregation in public schools was inherently unequal, violating the Fourteenth Amendment.

Beginning in 1964, the Congress passed the first of a series of Civil Rights Acts. It became self-evident under law that discrimination based upon race, sex, age, national origin and a list of other conditions was against the law. Among other things, the Acts acknowledged for the first time that children under the age of eighteen have civil rights.

Today it is self-evident that five hundred and forty-five Federal lawmakers, who are by and large lawyers, cannot do the thinking for two hundred and sixty million Americans. There is no need for Americans living today to compromise any longer. The era of human history wherein a few hundred people decide the fate of hundreds of millions of other humans is rapidly coming to an end. From a distance, Americans have witnessed the abject failure, dissolution and replacement of the socialist government of the Soviet Union. What we witnessed was the failure of a few hundred people trying to do the thinking for millions. This is also now the failure of the Federal Republics. When you have finished this book, I am confident you will agree that it is essential that we as Americans change our government and without delay.

PROPOSED CONSTITUTIONAL AMENDMENT

To effect a peaceful change to bring about the changes I'm advocating in this book, the U.S. Constitution needs to be amended as follows:

Change from Federal Republic

To National Democracy.

The Constitution of the United States is amended as follows:

1. Any law, tax, treaty, resolution, declaration of war, impeachment and/or any other act or motion whatsoever passed by Congress and signed into law by the President; or any of the same allowed to pass into law by the refusal of the President to sign; or any of the same allowed to pass by Congress due to an overriding of a Presidential veto, must then be submitted for approval or denial in the next general, or (in the case of war or impeachment) special election of the majority of the voters before it becomes effective or is rejected. The voters will at that time vote for or against the same approving or disapproving each facet of same, item by item. The congressional lawmaker's role is now one of advisement. Final approval or disapproval and/or renewal of all legislation rests solely with the will of the majority of voters.

2. When the Supreme Court passes judgement on the constitutional or unconstitutional nature of any issue, its ruling must then be voted upon and approved or disapproved, item by item, by the majority of voters in the next general election before the ruling takes effect or is nullified. The Supreme Court's role is now one of advisement. Final determination of constitutional and/or unconstitutional questions rests with the will of the majority of voters.

3.   Citizens have the right of National Referendum and Initiative in every general election. Their collective will as expressed by the approval or denial of legislation by the majority of voters is sovereign and therefore constitutional by definition. No act or decree of one, any or all the three branches of government can remove or deny the citizens' sovereignty. In every way the collective will of the majority as expressed by the majority in general and/or special elections of the citizens is sovereign over the three branches of government as well as all other affairs of the United States, its territories and its subjects. This includes but is not limited to the right to confirm or deny declarations of war, treaties, recall of elected officials and/or any other matter affecting affairs of State. Recalls may be for any reason. The majority has the absolute right to change or amend any existing law, any tax, any program, any commitment, any treaty of the United States of America made at any time including laws that they may have previously approved themselves and/or any of the above which were previously enacted into law by the prior representatives of the Federal Republic.   The will of the citizens as expressed by the majority of the voters is sovereign in every way with no exceptions.

4. The majority of Citizens have the sovereign right in General elections to confirm or deny each candidate for the Supreme Court as well as the right to remove any current Supreme Court Justice through the recall process in any general election for any reason.

5.   General elections will be held Nationally every three months until the majority of voters themselves approve a different schedule.

6. In the event of war, impeachment or direct threat to the national security, a special election may be called by either the Congress or the President. The President's emergency powers remain intact as written until changed or modified by the majority of voters. All other articles and prior Amendments of the Constitution which contradict this Amendment are hereby repealed.

METHOD OF ADOPTION:

AMENDMENT OR

CONSTITUTIONAL CONVENTION

Until Democracy is realized, the acid test for any candidate for President, Congress or the Supreme Court of for any other office should   be that they agree to this change. The new American President (or candidates for President) should forgo all other issues until the Federal Republic has been changed to   a National Democracy. The members of Congress or candidates for Congress should likewise forgo all other issues until the change has been made. The voters will decide and resolve all   other issues after they are sovereign.

The following are examples of how to proceed:

One: The President could ask Congress to adopt the Constitutional Amendment as described in the previous chapter if Congress has not already done so. All other issues except for those of ongoing National Security can and should wait.

If the Amendment as proposed above is forthcoming from Congress it will be then submitted to the individual states for ratification. If two-thirds of the States approve it the Amendment it will become the law of the land. The citizens will at last be sovereign.

The American President will have the unparalleled honor and distinction of being the last Chief Executive of the Federal Republic and the first of the National Democracy.   Whoever it is will be remembered forever in one breath with George Washington, Thomas Jefferson and Abraham Lincoln.

Two: If, within a reasonable time, the ratification of the Amendment is not forthcoming, either from the Congress or the individual states,   the President could convene a Constitutional Convention for its adoption and ratification. This convention could be convened live over the public airwaves and every citizen of voting age should be invited to participate as a delegate. By inviting every citizen to participate as a delegate   it will prevent the federal republicans now in office and the special interests which control them from rigging the delegate selection.

The President should chair the convention from beginning to end and limit proposals exclusively to the proposed amendment above. The President should explain the ramifications to the Nation prior to the convention. The Convention should take place over television and radio in every community and home in America and culminate in a special election called by the President.

This Constitutional Convention will be the first opportunity ever for the citizens to make law directly. As we the voters exercise our God-given right to change the nation from a Republic to a Democracy we will establish the processs in what will be recognized as the first National Referendum.

Three: If for some reason, one or another or both branches of Congress disagree with the method or process of the Constitutional Convention, the President does have the power under the Constitution to adjourn Congress until the Convention is over and the citizens have voted for or against sovereignty.

It is reasonable to expect that if existing Federal or State office holders truly believe in Democracy, they must be in favor of this Amendment and willing to take action now and not force the President to elect this third method. The lawmaker's willingness to set aside all other issues (except for those of national security) until the citizens are sovereign will be the acid test of their worthiness to remain in office.

They should demonstrate such belief and agreement by immediately setting aside all other issues and work for one and only one end until Democracy is realized. This issue alone will separate the sheep from the wolves among Congress and the government. The wolves will fight fang and claw to the end as I discuss in later chapters.

Once the voters are sovereign, under rule of National Democracy, the citizens will have the right of National Referendum. Through this process the majority of voters can, over time, decide whether voting should take place over a weekend, over the telephone or in whatever way makes the most sense to the majority. If the citizens pass a law and realize soon after that it was a mistake, they will have the power to change or modify it quickly--exactly the opposite of now.

If the citizens later decide to change the way elections are held, with computers to tabulate votes, it's easy enough to imagine that each person could have her or his own identification code. One person might prefer to use a number while another might prefer voice recognition and yet another the recorded sound of chirping birds or any other sound. It's all the same to a digital computer.

Safeguards can easily be built into the process. It is easy to see at this point that voter fraud could be made a capital offense if the citizens want such a law. But once the will of the majority of voters is sovereign, all issues including voting, taxes, laws, treaties, declarations of war, confirmation of Supreme Court nominees, recall or impeachment of any office holder including Supreme Court Justices would be by a vote of the majority.

General elections should be every three months until the voters get used to ruling themselves.

DEFINITIONS

The following are very brief and pragmatic definitions of different types of governments, movements and philosophies, an understanding of which is essential to the reader of this book. Hundreds of books have been written about each one. It's likely that proponents of each philosophy will take exception to mine. Nevertheless, it is necessary to offer them. In our nation, elected officials always refer to our government as a 'Democracy' or the 'Democratic Process'. Our Republic is neither one. It's no wonder the citizens are so confused. Today, Americans as a people don't have a Democracy. The federal republicans in power have Americans.

Federal Republics

Federal Republics are compromise governments originally founded upon the ideals of Democracy. Modern versions were fashioned as an attempt to approximate citizen-controlled governments by such eighteenth-century politicians as Thomas Jefferson and James Madison and others.

The United States, Germany, Mexico and dozens of other, mostly Western, nations have this form of government. Sovereign power over the nation is concentrated into the hands of a few hundred individuals who make up three branches of government-- Legislative, Executive and Judicial. Theoretically, the representatives of the Legislative and Executive offices are selected from among public candidates by the majority of voters in free elections.

In practice, the major political parties themselves hand-select the candidate of their ideological choice for each national office and back that person with the necessary funds to pay for a successful advertising campaign through primary and general elections. Occasionally an outsider to this strategy gets elected but unless he or she adopts the party line they are targeted and driven out in subsequent elections.

Whatever the officially-stated objectives of the government--such as protecting individual rights and freedoms--in practice the modern goal of those in power in the Federal Republics is to extend government control over all areas of human interaction, commerce and even the thoughts of its citizens under the guise of protecting the citizenry from oppressing one another or themselves.

Among other ideological contradictions of a Federal Republic in a industrial society are that a tiny number of individuals cannot adequately do the thinking for the millions of its citizenry. What the Federal Republics all have in common is that in order for the government to maintain its sovereignty, the ideals of Christianity and therefore freedom and self-government must be increasingly denied to the majority of citizens. Without exception in the industrial age, all the Federal Republics are bordering on totalitarianism.

Communism or Socialism

American politicians have always referred to socialist governments as communism. That's why I've included them both in one category. In the late nineteen century, Karl Marx, a German exile, political philosopher and economist wrote (in England) a book he titled, 'Das Capital'. He stated that Capitalism would eventually be so *successful* that eventually all physical labor would be replaced by machines everywhere on earth. In time, the machines would even be able to repair themselves. Eventually there would be unlimited quantities of everything for everyone. The commodities would all have to be given away for free because no one would have a job because no work would be necessary. (The people would have no wages to pay for any of the commodities.) He also said in Das Capital and other writings that there would therefore eventually be no need for private property or government. The machines and all capital would belong to the people who physically made them because the force of their labor would be physically embodied in the equipment. (This part can only be understood metaphysically.)

Total freedom for individuals was only supposed to be realized when Communism arrived at some distant time in the future. People who believe that capitalism (private ownership) and corporations (profits) are the cause of all social and economic problems are Marxists by historical definition, whether they know it or not. (Or will admit it.) The absolute necessity of management, allocation, marketing and risk are realities which are completely lost on Marxists.

According to Marx, selfishness and greed and all the other human vices including class oppression, racism, sexism and all other forms of injustice would wither away as Capitalism became ever more *successful*. Even Capitalism itself, which depended upon private ownership of the 'means of production', would eventually disappear evolving into communism. This was the famous, 'Contradiction of Capitalism' so often *misquoted and misunderstood* by Stalinist Communists who maintained capitalism would collapse due to financial failure.

Socialism was supposed to be a transition form of government between Capitalism and Communism to purposefully bring the latter about. Early twentieth century Russian politicians such as Nikolai Vladimir Lenin and in China, Mao Tse-Tung succeeded in urging their followers to violently overthrow their respective governments and annihilate the former rulers as well as any other opposition to insure a managed transition to Communism.

The excuse for concentrating power into the hands of a few hundred national leaders was that the average citizen needed to be protected by a small group who only had the collective interests of the average citizen in mind at all times. The ultimate goal of all Socialist governments was to export their type of government until all other forms of government were violently overthrown.

The ex-Soviet Union and the ex-Warsaw Pact nations plus China, Cuba, North Korea, Vietnam and over a dozen other countries have or until recently had variations of this form of government. Sovereign power over the nation is concentrated into the hands of a few hundred individuals who make up various branches of government. Theoretically, the representatives are selected from among public candidates by the majority of voters in free elections but in practice there is only one political Party. These are totalitarian governments with absolute sovereignty over its people.

There are variations in each country but in practice the Communist Party leaders themselves hand-select the person of their ideological choice and announce their selection to the voting citizenry. Occasionally an outsider to the Party philosophy acquires a degree of power, such as Leon Trotsky in the late 1910's and early 1920's in the Soviet Union and Chiang Ching in the 1960's and 1970's in China. But unless they are able to convince the majority of the

Party to join them in deposing the status quo, they are targeted and driven out and often put on trial. Anyone with a pro-Democracy idea is branded a counter-revolutionary and usually executed. The term, 'politically incorrect' originally came directly from the Chinese Cultural Revolution.

Whatever the officially stated objectives of the government, in practice the goal of Socialism or Communism is to extend government control over all areas of human interaction, thought and commerce under the guise of protecting the citizenry from themselves and the corrupting outside influences of capitalism.

The basic ideological contradiction of Socialism or Communism is that a tiny number of individuals cannot adequately do the thinking for the millions of its citizenry.

Also, in practice, what the these governments all have in common is that in order for the government to maintain its sovereignty, Christianity and therefore individual freedom must be denied to all of it's citizens except for those in the highest government office.

National Democracy

Defined in the first part and the point of this book. In essence, the citizen's will as expressed by the majority of voters in general elections or via referendum becomes the law of the land. Under Democracy the citizens are sovereign over the branches of government which exist only in an advisory capacity. Exactly the opposite of the Federal Republics and Communism. To date there are no National Democracies. Unless another country beats us to it, the United States will be the first one.

Parliamentary Government

A variation similar in practice to the Federal Republics except that historically this form of government has evolved from an absolute Monarchy. England and Canada have Parliaments with branches of government similar in function to those in United States. The Monarch is theoretically sovereign but she or he cannot refuse to approve any law passed by Parliament and remains as a figurehead.

The definition is not relevant to the point of this book except that once the United States becomes a Democracy, the citizens of countries with parliamentary governments will follow suit if they can overcome those few in power.

Anarchism

Anarchists generally believe that human nature is essentially good but that any form of government is inherently oppressive. They are usually well-educated but poor. They believe that if only governments were completely eliminated the citizens would naturally and spontaneously start cooperating with one another creating a more rational means of exchange apart from any government interference or supervision. Historically, anarchists are also known for going berserk and killing those whom they perceive to be their opponents. The contradiction for anarchists is that when governments completely break down within a country, the result isn't spontaneous cooperation but civil war. When governments break down between nations, the result is also war.

Laissez-faire Capitalism

Laissez-faire Capitalists generally believe that human nature is essentially selfish, and that any form of government is inherently restrictive. They believe that if only governments were restricted to protecting their own personal property rights and stabilizing the currency, the citizens would naturally and spontaneously be guided by their own selfish need to acquire commodities and wealth. The 'invisible hand' of the market place would always balance the supply of commodities with demand. Laissez-faire capitalists are generally wealthy but not well-educated. The contradiction for laissez-faire capitalists is that when a government breaks down within a country, the result isn't selfish, orderly cooperation but civil war. When governments break down between Nations, the result is also war.

Liberals, Left Wingers, Radicals and Commies

(Democrats)

In the 1990's, these are derogatory names Republicans call members of the Democrat Party or government employees, educators and Feminists. The contradiction here is in the name of the Party itself. In spite of its freedom-laced rhetoric and unceasing claims to the contrary, in the name of protecting the people from themselves, the Democrat Party is in practice the main organized political force in power attempting to change the U.S. Republic to a totalitarian government.

Conservatives, Right Wingers, and Homophobes

(Republicans)

In the 1990's, these are derogatory names Democrats call members of the Republican Party, the military, heterosexuals, those in business and Christians. The contradiction here is in the name of the Party itself. In spite of it's name, elements within the Republican Party are the only organized political force practicing and advocating any of the pro-Democracy ideals. It is the only currently organized political force in power that contains individual members who are preventing the Democrats from changing the U.S. into a totalitarian state. It is a battle that it has been losing by inches for decades.

Independents, Moderates, and Apathetic Voters

(United We Stand America, Inc.)

These are names for citizens of voting age not formally organized. It's worth noting that Ross Perot is attempting and may be succeeding in organizing this group into his United We Stand America, Inc., which is not really a non-profit political party but a private corporation. On the surface the company's rhetoric is somewhat pro-democracy but is far from complete. The irony is that the economic messages of this company are borrowed directly from the rank and file of local Republican Party politics. So far, Ross Perot's actual organization is the most centralized and authoritarian of the three and the most ideologically incomplete. The most basic and profound contradiction for the company is that Ross Perot is the only person from the United We Stand America, Inc. who seems to be allowed to voice a public opinion. In that, it appears to be wholly undemocratic.

ISSUES AFTER DEMOCRACY

When the United States of America is changed by you to a Democracy you will be able, for the first time, to participate and direct what happens next in this nation. The rest of this book is devoted to the resolution of the current issues facing us all after Democracy has been created.

Believe it or not there are perfectly elegant solutions to every complex issue. I've tried to address the major ones in this book. If I've left out the one closest to your heart, please forgive me. I am one person writing alone with limited resources. I hope to hear from many of you. Perhaps if this book is updated in the future I will include the best comments.

Before the first photographs of Earth were sent back from the manned lunar space ships, humans had no realistic image of what the Earth looked like, other than the fact it was round and reflected light. If you are too young to remember the depictions of the world before 1969 just look at any old movie or science book depicting the Earth. Just as with technology, the same is true for any social change. As a people, we won't really know exactly what deliciously new wonders Democracy will have for us until we deliberately make the changes advocated in this book. They are waiting for us only if enough of us choose to act right now.

I put it to you as fellow Americans, that you already know how to resolve the problems we're facing. But right now you have no political means to share and reach agreement with other citizens. All that will change forever once we have Democracy. The resolutions to the problems won't be exactly as I'm suggesting in this book. Perhaps very far from it. But of one fact I'm absolutely certain: The collective wisdom of Americans will bring forth perfectly eloquent solutions once we are sovereign.

AMERICAN ECONOMY REBORN

Under Democracy, we should put our economic house in order by putting our own people first for a change. This is our home after all. Few Americans ever leave the country even for vacation. We're not going anywhere.

Only a handful of Americans are billionaires. Less actually control multinational corporations. The United States of America belongs all Americans. We're not just a natural resource to be exploited by those who have the most money. Ross Perot's dream of 'Not For Sale At Any Price', is quite correct. It may take many years to undo the damage done in the last thirty by the five hundred and forty-five lawmakers to the American productive sector (where all wealth is created). But I'm more than confident that it can be fixed if Americans act now to create Democracy.

In the following sections, I outline steps that we should take once we are sovereign that would make our country's economic problems disappear so completely it will seem as if we never had any to start with.

INCOME TAXES

*'Americans have forgotten that the
War of Independence
began over a tax on tea.'*

John Pepka

It takes knowledge, dedication, money, skill, hard work and good luck to build a nation's economy. Any fool can raise taxes to pay people to produce nothing. Any fool does.

When you go to the grocery store you don't hand over 50% of your cash and take whatever the absentee managers have already decided should go into your basket, especially if you know that the value of the goods is much less than half of what they are charging. When purchasing cars or homes it's no different. Only apologists of totalitarian governments believe the above would be a rational system. Yet all the Federal Republics in the world do the same thing to their citizens. It's called 'paying the federal income tax'.

This nation existed until World War I without a permanent income tax. When one was first imposed the average person paid only one percent.

The Federal Reserve System, which is controlled through a political patronage appointment by the President, deliberately expands the money supply faster than the rate of growth of the Net Domestic Product to create inflation. Inflation drives everyone into a higher income tax bracket without increasing your real purchasing power. Inflation has the same effect on real estate tax values.

The government tells us how much better off we are because we have more printed dollars. The economic term for this is, 'Money Illusion'. They get the value of your money. You get to keep the illusion. In a graduated tax system, which we have, the citizens then have the *honor* of paying more taxes and at a higher rate.

Today the average person pays half of her income for taxes of various kinds. You produce value for the economy. You contribute half your money so the five hundred and forty-five can pay it to themselves and their reserve army of loyal voters who get paid to produce nothing. Get it?

You're right! The current system is not rational. Americans are extremely generous as a people and as a nation. There is no parallel in history to our generosity. That the U.S. citizens have put up with the tax system we have up until now proves our unbridled generosity beyond any question.

The majority of the five hundred and forty-five lawmakers in Washington D.C. are declaring through the current tax system that Americans are unqualified to decide for themselves how to spend their own money. Americans are told that the complexities of the issues are too much for us to comprehend. If the Nation's problems are out of control, and they are, it is the situational ethics of the lawmakers themselves that have made it so. They are wrong. The citizen's answer to such contempt must be with our own direct action.

All this will change under Democracy when the voters decide item by item what taxes will be levied and how they will be spent. At a minimum each and every current spending commitment will have to be re-approved by the voters item by item. In that sense, under National Democracy, all taxes will be voluntary. But I have a better plan.

For non-economists it takes some explaining (the likely topic of a future book) but in the next chapter on the Budget, I spell out in dollars and cents exactly what I think would work to revive the economy in the United States. The National Democracy will deliver a thriving economy where everyone who wants a job will have a good one. I propose among other changes that both personal and corporate Federal income taxes be removed permanently. If you like my budget, you the citizens will have to order it done. But I warn you that will only be possible after you have changed the government from a Republic to a Democracy.

BALANCED BUDGET

The Democrats in the House and Senate gladly let Bill Clinton's name be associated with the so-called *'Clinton Deficit Reduction Plan'* which passed into law August 1993. They knew the name was a lie and that the plan will fail. It was nothing more than a new tax increase. It will result in at least another one trillion dollars being added to the already four trillion dollar deficit by the end of fiscal 1998.

American citizens don't have to wait five or ten years for the five hundred and forty-five lawmakers to balance the Federal budget (the so-called *'Balanced Budget Amendment'* the lawmakers are currently debating will not be binding even if it is passed and ratified).

In the first General Election, held ninety days after National Democracy is realized, the citizens could order the budget balanced immediately by cutting every spending program across the board. But I have an even better plan.

Regarding my own budget proposal for National Democracy, below I illustrate several changes to be made simultaneously. Some of the ideas are quite new and may come as a pleasant shock at first. But I've studied the government's official budget and economic models at length and I'm convinced mine is far superior to the current system under the Federal Republic. (My university training was in business and economics and I have worked in investments and finance since I was first licensed under the NASD in 1978.)

Specifically the changes have to do with wealth creation, power, taxes, risk and the money supply. I suggest if you're not an economist that you use the index to read or re-read those topics before continuing. The actual numbers which follow don't tell the entire story so I have included a few comments on the changes. In no way can these brief explanations be taken as a complete review but I include them anyway to help the reader not trained in economics understand the basics.

Any other additional national expenditures can and will be made if initiated by the voters through National Referendum or suggested by Congress, accepted by the President and then approved by the citizens in the next general or special election.

Outlined below is written description of the basics of my plan for a National Democracy baseline budget (actual numbers follow):

First: I propose that all personal and corporate Federal income taxes be eliminated permanently. This one act would remove all barriers to wealth creation and therefore would stimulate the private and productive economy as no other act. It would also instantly attract hundreds of billions of dollars if not a trillion of new foreign investment to America.

In the eighteen months following the elimination of all income taxes there would be approximately ten million net jobs created in the private sector most of which would be in industry and commerce. Beginning immediately the Net Domestic Product (NDP) would surge. I calculate that, after the initial surge, (which could be as high as twenty percent in the first eighteen months) the NDP growth rate would level off to between twelve to fifteen percent annually. With my model these net rates of growth will be easily sustained for at least a decade with no recession. During that time, I estimate there would be a net gain of at least forty million new jobs. (I use a conservative twelve percent rate of growth in my budget model which follows these explanations.) Countries with no income taxes have for decades sustained uninterrupted net growth rates averaging in the high teens. The United States had sustained annual growth rates averaging in the teens for a century prior to the imposition of permanent income taxes.

Second: The Federal Reserve Board's function would be changed slightly. Very briefly, the 'Fed' (as insiders refer to it) currently expands the money supply by either lowering the 'reserve requirements' of Member banks or by lending new money to Member banks who in turn lend the money to other commercial banks at interest who then lend it to all other borrowers at even higher interest rates. That's how the Federal Government gets new money into circulation.

The actual number of dollars in circulation is called M1. The same dollar is usually spent several times during the year as it passes from borrower to investor to employee to retailer and so on. The rate the same dollar is spent per year is known as velocity. Basically M1 multiplied by the velocity equals M2.

There is another index called M3 but it's less significant to the budget I'm proposing and I won't go into it. (Obviously only the minds of a banker and a politician meshing together could have designed the existing monetary system.)   Under my plan the expansion of the money supply would be tied directly to the growth of the Net Domestic Product (unlike now).   Instead of the Fed lending new money (the growth of M1) to banks at interest, the new money would go directly to the Congress, without interest, to spend to run the government. My budget below projects and illustrates the amounts under the revenue title   'New Money'. The velocity of New Money injected into the economy through the government would be just slightly   slower than under the current Fed system where borrowed money must be put to work immediately. I use a velocity factor of six (6) but only for the New Money the government spends {as the New Money of M1 is spent by the government and becomes M2 in the rest of the economy where the velocity factor is seven (7)}.

Third: The debt of the United States Government would be restructured. Right now the notes and bonds that the U.S. Treasury sells are fixed interest bearing certificates. They are non-callable (unlike most private debt or debt of other nations).   Simply, non-callable means that under the Republic, the U.S. Government can't (meaning won't) refinance its older long-term debt certificates at current lower interest rates. Most other countries refinance. (U.S. politicians in general don't display any evidence that they understand economics and those that do are afraid of loosing face.)

The United States currently has over four trillion dollars of debt and will pay over three hundred billion in interest for this year alone.   That is an effective average interest rate of eight percent overall. In my budget (under the National Democracy) all the notes and bonds issued by the Federal Republic would be recalled and reissued at current three percent rates. These replacement notes and bonds would be callable and guaranteed by the National Democracy. No lender would loose a penny of principle. None would loose any current interest. The net savings to the nation in the first year alone would be two hundred billion dollars in saved interest. It's exactly like refinancing a home to get a lower interest rate. That's known as common sense.

Fourth: All but a token of land-based U.S. Army forces would be withdrawn from the nations of Germany and Japan, placed on Reserve, and given new jobs in industry. I discuss the reasons for this in several of the other chapters. This act alone would cut one hundred billion dollars annually from the military budget.   The citizens may vote any for any increase in military spending.

Fifth: Unlike the current Federal Republic, the National Democracy of the United States of America should never   allow money to be borrowed to pay for such things as the purchase of art. Issues of taste in art or censorship aside, until the Government is in the 'black' (profitable) we can't afford it. By initiative the sovereign citizens can of course approve any individual purchase of art that they collectively want that they are willing to pay for in cash.

Art and films won't stop being created and purchased just because the National Democracy temporarily stops purchasing it with borrowed money. Under my budget and through tax savings the citizens would average a trillion extra dollars of disposable income to spend every year for the next five years and more than that every year thereafter. They can then decide for themselves how it should be spent. Tens of millions of those extra dollars will be spent on art.

The hundreds of millions of dollars currently being borrowed annually to pay for Art when there are so many more important issues (such changing the Social Security system into a true retirement investment program and   paying down the national debt) is a testimony to the tragic lack of wisdom of our current leaders.

Sixth: All political patronage and/or   redundant federal departments or programs would be eliminated or severely curtailed. This includes the Departments of Education, Energy, Foundation on the Arts and Humanities and the most of the funding for the U.S. Information Agency.

With few exceptions, all other Departments would have their budgets cut by at least twenty percent. The cuts should be made in government workers wages to bring the maximum wage in line with per capita income rates. This is not as bad as it sounds for Federal workers since, if all Federal income taxes are removed, the average Federal worker will have close to the same purchasing power as before. (They would be called National workers.)

Those in government would also have a new incentive. Their overriding goal would be to help those in the private sector to become more efficient and therefore to produce higher average earnings. It would be the only way for National workers to earn a collective raise in their own wages. There would be tens of millions of new jobs created almost immediately in the private sector for those who won't wish to continue in National employment under the new conditions.

The only absolute spending increase that I recommend is for NASA for all the reasons I give in the chapter on Space Exploration.

Seventh: The New Social Security Retirement Plan would be inaugurated and turned over to the National Association of Securities Dealers Member Firms to manage as I describe in my chapter on that subject. The National Democracy would assume all guarantees and promises made to existing retirees by the Federal Republic. But each employee making current contributions would have her or his own individual vested account. The plan would be phased in over the next ten years.

Each account would include disability, and life insurance benefits. However, these benefits would be acquired from private insurance carriers at a fraction of the existing government's overhead cost. The chapter on Social Security has more details on what I propose including the National Democracy's government guarantees.

Eighth: All agricultural subsidies and guarantees would be eliminated. Tobacco subsidies would also be eliminated as a matter of Public Health. Since farmers would no longer have to pay Federal income taxes, they would easily be able to buy less expensive private insurance from private carriers to cover their various risks.

Ninth: In the years when the Net Domestic Product grows by more than twelve percent, the expansion of the money supply (New Money) would be used to reduce the deficit by retiring debt. Outstanding notes and bonds would be recalled according to a formula to be worked out later. There would be no non-recallable debt.

For those anti-Democracy agents who will criticize my plan (to remove all income taxes) as 'caving into the rich' as well as for those who *are* rich who might see my budget only as an opportunity to exploit American workers I have this warning: Once Americans create National Democracy they will be sovereign.   If higher wages aren't forthcoming from productivity gains within a particular industry *the citizens will have the collective power to order <u>any</u> remedy.* I doubt seriously if there will be many examples like the Disney conglomerate where the C.E.O. is compensated in hundreds of millions while the average employee is paid tens of thousands.

In spite of divisive government propaganda to the contrary, the average worker in private industry understands that the worst 'crime' a company can commit against its employees and shareholders is to fail to make a profit. 'No profits' is the first sign of economic collapse and quickly translates to 'no jobs'. Profits must be judiciously balanced between being retained by the business for new capital purchases and being paid out in employee bonuses or dividends for shareholders (few corporations actually pay dividends and it doesn't diminish the market value of their shares.)

The majority of Americans possess the wisdom to know not to kill the geese that lays the golden eggs. The only ones who don't seem to possess such wisdom are the Democrats in federal office and their federally funded legions (including most of the social science professors at American collages and universities).

I think you will agree after you study my National Democracy budget that, not only is it a more equitable plan than the current one offered by the existing five hundred and forty-five lawmakers but it is more rational. (Something quite new for government.)

The following is a comparison of the current baseline budget of the U.S. Federal Republic to my own proposed baseline budget for the U.S. National Democracy:

Balanced Budget

Current Official Baseline Budget Of U.S. Federal Republic:
Total Adjusted For Bill Clinton's New Deficit Reduction Tax
(from the 1993 Federal Publication)

vs.

Proposed Baseline Budget of National Democracy
(from Vincent Mountjoy-Pepka)

Economic Projections
Federal Republic

Gross Domestic Product (GDP)
Dollars in Billions

	1993	1994	1995	1996	1997	1998
Current Dollars	6,254	6,594	6,942	7,288	7,626	7,952
Percent Change	5.4	5.4	5.2	4.9	4.5	4.1
Constant Dollars (1987 = 100)	5,054	5,204	5,354	5,497	5,628	5,740
Percent Change	2.4	2.4	2.3	2.3	2.2	2.2
CPI (Inflation)	3	2.7	2.7	2.7	2.7	2.7
Unemployment Rate	7.1	6.6	6.2	5.9	5.8	5.7

Economic Projections
National Democracy

Gross Domestic Product (GDP)
Dollars in Billions

	1993	1994	1995	1996	1997	1998
Current Dollars	6,254	7,004	7,845	8,786	9,841	11,022
Percent Change	5.4	12	12	12	12	12
Constant Dollars (1987 = 100)	5,054	5,559	6,171	6,911	7,741	8,670
Percent Change	2.4	10	11	12	12	12
CPI (Inflation)	3	2	1	0	0	0
Unemployment Rate	7.1	4	3	2	1	1

Balanced Budget

Baseline Receipts By Source
Dollars in Billions

	1993	1994	1995	1996	1997	1998
Individual Income Taxes	516	537	574	611	635	662
Corporation Income Taxes	109	114	118	122	122	126
Social Insurance Taxes	427	462	485	510	530	552
Excise Taxes	48	49	50	47	48	49
Other	50	54	58	61	63	66
Totals	1,149	1,215	1,284	1,350	1,398	1,454

Economic Projections
National Democracy

Baseline Receipts By Source
Dollars in Billions

	1993	1994	1995	1996	1997	1998
Individual Income Taxes	516	0	0	0	0	0
Corporation Income Taxes	109	0	0	0	0	0
New Money	0	140	157	176	197	220
Social Insurance Retirement (a)	427	478	535	599	671	752
Excise Taxes (b)	48	53	60	67	75	84
Other (b)	50	56	62	70	78	88
Totals	1,149	727	814	911	1,021	1,144

(a) Increase in amounts reflects the increase in the numbers of people working and not an increase in S.S. tax rates.

(b) Increases due to the higher growth of the GDP and not to an increase in tax rates.

Balanced Budget

Current Services Outlays By Agency
Dollars in Billions

	1993	1994	1995	1996	1997	1998
Cabinet Agencies:						
Agriculture	66.5	62.3	62.2	63.2	63.6	64.3
Commerce	3.1	3.0	3.2	3.5	3.6	3.6
Defense	277.3	270.1	269.4	269.4	271.0	273.1
Education	30.5	30.5	29.9	25.6	29.8	30.7
Energy	17.5	17.5	18.1	18.3	18.8	19.2
Health and						
Human Services	590.6	641.6	690.3	742.3	800.0	857.5
on-budget	(291.8)	(327.4)	(361.3)	(398.1)	(440.2)	(481.4)
off-budget	(298.8)	(314.2)	(329.0)	(344.1)	(359.9)	(376.1)
Housing &	25.3	27.5	29.4	30.1	30.3	30.8
Urban Development						
Interior	7.1	7.1	7.3	7.6	7.7	8.0
Justice	10.6	10.3	11.1	11.1	11.1	11.5
Labor	42.8	34.7	34.4	34.7	35.3	35.9
State	5.3	5.6	5.8	6.0	6.2	6.4
Transport	35.9	36.6	37.5	38.4	39.6	40.5
Treasury	301.5	320.6	347.7	374.9	402.0	432.1
Veterans	35.3	37.7	37.6	37.2	39.4	40.8
Major Agencies:						
Corps of Engineers,						
Military Retire &						
Other Defense	29.5	30.7	32.0	33.2	34.4	35.7
E.P.A.	6.4	6.6	6.9	7.1	7.3	7.4
Office of Pres.	0.2	0.2	0.2	0.2	0.3	0.3
Emergency Man	3.1	1.9	1.4	1.1	1.0	1.0
Funds for President	11.8	12.0	11.8	11.9	12.0	12.3
General Services	1.3	0.9	1.4	0.4	0.4	0.4
Judicial	2.5	2.6	2.7	2.8	2.9	3.0
Legislative	2.8	2.9	3.0	3.1	3.2	3.3
NASA	14.1	14.5	14.9	15.4	15.8	16.2
National Science	2.8	2.8	2.8	2.9	3.0	3.1
Personnel Man	37.2	38.8	40.1	43.8	47.0	49.5
Postal Service	1.6	1.6	1.3	(0.7)	(1.1)	(1.4)
Railroad Retirement	4.8	4.8	4.8	4.8	4.8	4.8
Small Business	0.8	0.7	0.5	0.5	0.6	0.6
All Other	9.6	15.4	7.2	(4.2)	(1.9)	2.2
Undistributed	(119.0)	(124.9)	(130.0)	(136.3)	(143.3)	(151.1)
Receipts						
on-budget	(85.6)	(88.6)	(90.0)	(92.0)	(93.7)	(95.7)
off-budget	(33.3)	(36.3)	(40.0)	(44.3)	(49.6)	(55.4)
Total Outlays	1,459	1,517	1,585	1,648	1,745	1,842
Total Receipts	1,149	1,215	1,284	1,350	1,398	1,454
Annual Deficits	(310)	(301)	(301)	(298)	(347)	(388)
(Proj. Deficits of Mr.						
Clinton's Tax Plan)	(317)	(255)	(230)	(188)	(181)	(202)

Balanced Budget

Baseline Services Outlays By Agency
Dollars in Billions

	1993	1994	1995	1996	1997	1998
Cabinet Agencies:						
Agriculture (1)	66.5	15.6	15.6	15.8	15.9	16.1
Commerce	3.1	3.0	3.2	3.5	3.6	3.6
Defense (2)	277.3	170.1	169.4	169.4	171.0	173.1
Education (3)(a)	30.5	0.0	0.0	0.0	0.0	0.0
Energy (4)	17.5	1.5	1.5	1.5	1.5	1.5
Health and						
Human Services	590.6	227.4	227.4	227.4	227.4	227.4
on-budget (5)	(291.8)	(227.4)	(227.4)	(227.4)	(227.4)	(227.4)
off-budget (6)	(298.8)	0.0	0.0	0.0	0.0	0.0
Housing & Urban						
Development (7)	25.3	10.5	11.2	11.4	11.5	11.7
Interior (7)	7.1	2.7	2.8	2.9	2.9	3.0
Justice	10.6	9.5	9.5	9.5	9.5	9.5
Labor (3)	42.8	3.5	3.4	3.5	3.5	3.6
State	5.3	2.1	2.2	2.3	2.4	2.4
Transport (7)	35.9	3.7	3.8	3.8	4.0	4.1
Treasury (8)	301.5	128.0	128.0	128.0	128.0	128.0
Veterans	35.3	30.2	30.1	29.8	31.5	32.6
Major Agencies:						
Corps of Engineers,						
Military Retire &						
Other Defence (7)	29.5	3.1	3.2	3.3	3.4	3.6
E.P.A.	6.4	4.6	4.8	5.0	5.1	5.2
Office of Pres.	0.2	0.2	0.2	0.2	0.2	0.2
Emergency Man	3.1	1.9	1.4	1.1	1.0	1.0
President (7)	11.8	4.8	4.7	4.8	4.8	4.9
General Services	1.3	0.9	1.4	0.4	0.4	0.4
Judicial	2.5	2.1	2.2	2.2	2.3	2.4
Legislative	2.8	1.5	1.5	1.6	1.6	1.7
NASA	14.1	14.1	30.0	35.0	40.0	45.0
National Science	2.8	2.8	2.8	2.9	3.0	3.1
Personnel Man (3)	37.2	5.8	6.0	6.6	7.1	7.4
Postal Service	1.6	1.6	1.3	(0.7)	(1.1)	(1.4)
Railroad Retirement	4.8	4.8	4.8	4.8	4.8	4.8
Small Business	0.8	0.7	0.5	0.5	0.6	0.6
All Other (7)	9.6	2.5	2.5	(4.2)	(1.9)	2.2
Undistributed						
Receipts	(119)	(125)	(130)	(136)	(143)	(151)
on-budget	(85.6)	(88.6)	(90.0)	(92.0)	(93.7)	(95.7)
off-budget	(33.3)	(36.3)	(40.0)	(44.3)	(49.6)	(55.4)
Total Outlays	1,459	534	545	536	541	547
Total Receipts	1,149	727	814	911	1,021	1,144
Annual Deficits						
Or Surplus (9)	(310)	193	269	376	480	597

Balanced Budget

(Note) The maximum Federal Employee wage to be equal to the average for all working Americans (see formula in chapter titled 'Productive Vs. Nonproductive'). The projected savings for every Department or Program has been adjusted for this formula. NASA is the only possible exception as it is the only productive agency of government (refer to chapter on Space Development).

(1) Food Stamp and school lunch programs to continue at current levels minus the wasteful overhead. All other agricultural subsidy programs to be canceled unless the Citizens vote to approve continuance by raising taxes. Food prices during temporary shortages will be stabilized with imports and not through ongoing subsidies.

(2) Military withdrawal from Germany and Japan (Army & Air Force) will save 100 billion per year beginning in 1994.

(3) Redundant and patronage programs to be canceled or severely modified unless Citizens vote to continue by raising taxes on an item by item basis. (a) The Federally Insured Student Loan Program to be taken over and administered by Human Services.

(4) Department of Energy to oversee disposal of nuclear waste.

(5) See chapters on National Health Insurance and Social Security for explanations of savings. Also the lowering of the unemployment rate and lowering of the inflation rate will drive down the need for increasing expenditures.

(6) Beginning in 1994 the 'off budget' loans from the Social Security Trust Fund to finance the deficit will end. The New Social Security Retirement program will begin with funds listed below in (9) and will be administered by the NASD according to vested provisions.

(7) All additional spending projects to be approved item by item by majority of voters.

(8) Treasury savings through recall and refinancing of National debt at short term rates.

(9) These surpluses to belong to the New Social Security Retirement program. It is to be administered by the NASD and invested in U.S. corporations by professional money managers. Each current contributor will have a separate vested account. In future years when the surpluses exceed the amount collected under the New Social Security Retirement Plan they are to be used to retire the deficit.

Net Annual Tax Savings Available For Private Job Creation Under National Democracy Plan If Enacted In 1994. (In billions)

	1993	1994	1995	1996	1997	1998
Individual Income Saved	(516)	537	574	611	635	662
Corporation Income Saved	(109)	114	118	122	122	126
Deficit or Surplus (9)	(310)	193	269	376	480	597
Totals	(935)	844	960	1,108	1,237	1,385

With the National Democracy baseline budget, at a minimum and by the end of 1998, Americans would save five trillion extra dollars of private wealth and thereby annually create at least five million net new jobs. There would be no interruptions in essential services. If the Federal Government continues unchanged (Mr. Clinton's so-called deficit reduction tax passed into law, August 1993) by 1998 another one trillion dollars of debt will be added to the Federal Deficit bringing the total to over five trillion That's $ 5,000,000,000,000.

The New Social Security Retirement Plan will begin immediately and will run concurrently with the Old Social Security Plan until the latter is phased out through time by attrition. The New Plan is to be phased in for all current contributors to Social Security (9). Those already retired or disabled to continue indefinitely under the existing plan with the current conditions. The new plan will no longer be a tax but phased over the next ten years in as a true investment program administered by the National Association of Securities Dealers with additional life and disability insurance for all working Americans and their families. (Read the chapter on Social Security.)

As noted in the first part of this chapter, this budget would not eliminate any essential government services. The citizens can vote to voluntarily add any new taxes to complete any specific projects such as a highway or any other item the majority agrees upon. (They could also vote to eliminate or modify anything in the baseline budget.) There is nothing to prevent citizens from individual regions from voting to tax themselves to create or complete an agreed upon project. It is likely that the first voluntary taxes to be added will be for local schools.

GLOBAL COMPETITION

Under Democracy we should start to rebuild our economy by voting to stop spending money and precious resources to protect our economic competitors from their former enemies. For instance, over the past fifty years the United States Government has spent over a trillion dollars protecting Japan and Germany from their former enemies (who were ironically our former allies). At the same time, our Nation has given preferred trade agreements and unlimited free technology to these and several other countries. Our people, with calculated incentives from our own government, have purchased virtually everything these countries could produce for export, but unfortunately with little reciprocity.

Since under Democracy American voters will renew, approve or disapprove all trade agreements and treaties, we will be able to see just how competitively Japan can produce personal computers or anything else after it starts spending precious capital and manpower defending itself from China and Korea. From whom does Germany need to be protected?

Americans should also consider that the United States has made war reparations to thousands of Japanese wrongly interned in concentration camps during World War II and to their decedents. After serious consideration, Americans may want tie any future trade agreements with Japan to the war reparations Japan agrees to pay to the survivors and their families and descendents of the tens of millions in China, Korea, Philippines and the other Asian nations that were displaced, enslaved or murdered when Japan invaded and conquered their countries during World War II.

In the case of China, Japan ruled Manchuria for over a decade. As they say in Washington D.C. (but don't mean), 'We need to level the playing field'.

FOREIGN TRADE

How many of you remember voting in 1982 for most if not all trade tariffs to be taken off? They were removed so the five hundred and forty-five lawmakers could transfer wealth from our capital economy into the hands of foreigners (mostly Asians) and back to themselves in the form of Asian loans to our government so the politicians would have more money to spend without raising our taxes directly. The same thing is happening on a much smaller scale with Mexico.

As a group, the five hundred and forty-five lawmakers think they know more than the other two hundred sixty million Americans. Based upon their track record over the past thirty years, there is no evidence to support that attitude. The opposite is true.

When the last manufacturing job has been transferred out of the United States, what will Americans have to trade for the imported commodities? Only real estate and ourselves. Once Americans have a Democracy, the citizens will be able to vote to approve, disapprove or renew all trade agreements item by item. There would have to be an obvious, direct and understandable benefit to the average citizen or the treaty should not be approved by the majority.

The November 1993 vote to approve the proposed North American Free Trade Agreement (NAFTA) should have been shelved until after the Constitution is amended to create National Democracy. Whatever the pros or cons, the decision rightly belongs to the majority of the two hundred sixty million American citizens and not to the existing lame duck lawmakers of the Federal Republic.

After Democracy, the voters should rule it treason for a government official to accept a payment of any kind from any foreign agent or to accept any remuneration of any kind (other than their own ordinary income) after their term of office has expired.

Foreign businessmen should have to approach the American people first through their own embassies. If they want Americans to approve a particular trade agreement they can convince us directly and openly in the same way anyone else convinces us to spend our money: Let the foreign lobbyists identify themselves and run ads in the newspaper and on television and radio. If this is an unsophisticated or unworkable perspective the citizens will discover it.

OPERATION SCUTTLE ENDS

The phrase, 'Global Economics' is not new but the five hundred and forty-five lawmakers began to parrot it incessantly in the early nineteen eighties. They scrambled to find new slogans to disguise what they were planning. They were searching for new buyers for the certificates of U.S. debt in order to finance their deficit spending binge. To date, the global economic scheme has increased the national deficit to four trillion dollars. Japanese businessmen understood and appreciated better than our own leaders that ownership and control over manufacturing is and has always been the absolute foundation to create wealth.

It is a simple equation. In exchange for a virtual total lifting of import duties and quotas, the five hundred and forty-five lawmakers sold off the manufacturing base of our country so that the Japanese and other world bankers would buy U.S. debt. That's why, at the time, the politicians in Washington D.C. did not insist upon the unilateral elimination of trade barriers in Japan and the other so-called 'trading partner' nations. All the politicians wanted was to sell more debt to raise cash. They knew they personally didn't have to pay it back. The borrowed money was used, in addition to all the other trillions of dollars collected in taxes, to pay government employees, welfare recipients and others to produce nothing. The five hundred and forty-five knew exactly what they were doing, however much they deny it. It was no conspiracy, just 'politics as usual'.

It's interesting that Charles Keating Jr. was held personally liable, tried for criminal mismanagement of, and convicted of squandering two and a half billion dollars of Lincoln Savings & Loan's assets. He was sentenced to prison by both State and Federal Courts. He will be there for a very long time. Once Americans are sovereign over the three branches of government, the majority may demand and receive a personal accounting from the five hundred and forty-five lawmakers for the multi-trillions of dollars squandered just since 1980.

NUCLEAR WEAPONS

Under Democracy, Americans should consider cutting by half the billions of dollars being spent annually on the development, support and deployment of nuclear weapons. The nuclear arms build up was not about defense as much as it was about the five hundred and forty-five Federal lawmakers who rule our nation transferring wealth and power away from U.S. citizens and into the hands of those who would vote for them and give large donations.

In Japan, nine out of ten scientists work for industry. Nine out of ten of our scientists work directly or indirectly for the military. Those who labor to create and deploy nuclear weapons consume expensive scarce natural resources but produce nothing of direct or indirect material value. We can never use the massive numbers of nuclear weapons unless we want all life on the planet to end. ICBMs and nuclear submarines have no scrap value whatsoever. However necessary some of these weapons may be in today's world, the citizens have the right to put things into their own perspective.

In my opinion, the Cold War collapsed in spite of, and not because of, the massive nuclear build up over the past thirty years (much to the private disappointment of the most militant of the five hundred and forty-five).

One nuclear-armed cruse missile launched from a World War II IOWA Class battle ship would have been enough to obliterate Baghdad and put an instant end to the Persian Gulf War if President Bush had wanted to deploy it. A ship of that description did in fact fire the first Allied salvo and it was a non-nuclear cruise missile. (The majority of U.S. citizens should have the final say over all weapons creation and terms of deployment.)

Using conventional weapons, our Air Force, Army and Navy can repel any invasion force before it even leaves the enemy shore. Personally I think the money expended on fighter planes is extremely well spent and I'd like to see Americans vote to increase spending in that area, if for no other reason than that many of the pilots end up flying in the nation's airliners.

Let our scientists go to work on something productive and useful. Considering the trillions of dollars Americans have spent educating and keeping them in luxury for the past three decades it's time we got something of real value back.

Many Americans cling to the notion that Ronald Reagan brought down the Soviet Union with military spending in the same way that very young children cling to their stuffed teddy bears for comfort. The more confused they get by reality the harder they hold to the delusion. World War II had the same effect on many Americans of the depression era. In their minds that war was more than necessary, it was 'good' because the war was perceived to have brought national economic recovery.

John Maynard Keynes, an Englishman considered to be the 'father' of modern economics, first realized that the 'Great Depression' of the 1930's was caused by the contraction of the money supply under President Herbert Hoover's administration. Expanding the money supply to stimulate unused industrial capacity ended the depression (under FDR). The government could have spent the money on anything or handed out dollars for free until the industrial capacity reached full employment. This would have had the same effect only better since the world-wide depression would have ended sooner. The money would not have been wasted on war machinery. Americans would not have been confused over the issue of military spending being 'good' for the economy for the next sixty years. It's likely that without Hoover's blundering appointee there would have been no U.S. depression in the first place and no accompanying worldwide depression as the American markets collapsed. This would have meant that Adolph Hitler could have not come to power the way he did. Second World War may not have occurred. What happens in the United States affects everything one way or another.

After Democracy is created, Americans will live in a more rational Nation. People won't be afraid to think and act together. The wisdom of the majority will decide what to do to defend our Nation by voting in a new policy. To God who gave us our rights, let it not be said of this new generation of Americans that, 'We were afraid so we hid our talents in the ground' (nuclear silos). Let us hear instead, 'Well done good and faithful servants. You could be trusted with little, so enter into the joy of the Creator. Come and share in even greater wealth.'

WEALTH

*'What good is it for a man to gain
the whole world, yet forfeit his soul?'*

Jesus Christ

Most of Jesus's admonitions were for the lawmakers of his day although his principles apply to everyone for all time. Under Democracy, without the majority of the five hundred and forty-five lawmakers to confuse and loot us, Americans will quickly relearn that all wealth is and has to be physically created and that manufacturing is the single most important industry, the one on which all the others depend.

That large segments of our society question this is the most fitting tribute to just how confused they've become from listening to the majority of the five hundred and forty-five lawmakers in Washington D.C. It is a profoundly basic truth that if not for manufacturing, farmers would still be covered with animal skins and planting seeds in the ground with sticks. The examples are endless.

If what the citizens need creates too much pollution, it means that we need more technology and resources to produce things, not less. In the chapters on Space Exploration and the Military, I describe how we need to begin to move our industrial base off of the planet.

In the meantime there should be, at a bare minimum, a total and permanent capital gains tax exemption for investors who invest in American manufacturing corporations that are vertically integrated in the U.S. economy. Vertical integration in this context would mean a company employs only Americans and conducts all or virtually all of their manufacturing operations in this country. At the same time there should be a complete and permanent income tax exemption for wholly integrated American manufacturing corporations. (But an even better plan is outlined in the chapters titled Income Tax and Budget.)

As for the Value Added and income surtaxes, health care payroll tax, or any other of the other taxes President Bill Clinton or any Democrat proposes, I have this to say: If a trillion and a half dollars of spending in the next fiscal year can't accomplish what the five hundred and forty-five lawmakers want, what will new taxes do except further scuttle the economy?

It's the employees, managers, salespeople, owners and investors all working together that brings about prosperity for any company. The nations of the Common Market set limits on the number of cars within the Common Market to be sold that are manufactured outside of Common Market nations. Why? The answer should be obvious to all but the looters in Washington D.C.

RISK

The highest income earners in the world get most of their income from investments. This means they have put their money at risk to create new wealth. They are looking for what is commonly referred to as a capital gain. They can and often do lose up to 100% and at times even more of the money they have invested. Yet they are expected to pay out 36% (plus an additional 10% under certain circumstances) under Mr. Clinton's and the Democrat's latest tax increase (Passed August 1993).

Most new businesses have modest beginnings. For example, five investors join together and each puts $10,000 dollars at risk to start a new business. Usually one or more of them will manage it on a day-to-day basis, giving up the opportunity to earn wages elsewhere. And typically, they do this for far less money than they were earning elsewhere. The new company hires other employees, rents space, buys equipment, pays city, state and municipal taxes, etc.

The odds of success are not good. After three years sixty percent of such new business will be out of business with all the original money lost and usually much more additional money lost as well. Thirty percent will not have grown beyond the start up phase. Only ten percent will have done well. If the one out of ten who are successful need additional money to expand the businesses the owners usually have to bring in additional investors. (Banks are now in the risk avoidance business) But, if they do this by selling some of their original stock, it is a taxable event to them. It is treated as a capital gain.

In the United States there are almost the same number of businesses that start up each year as those that go out of business. Typically it's not just the assets of the business that are lost but also most of the other assets the original investors had as well (because of personal liability). These new start-up companies are providing most of the jobs in America yet they are the least appreciated and most penalized by the five hundred and forty-five lawmakers in Washington D.C. and their counterparts in state governments.

Compare the risk employers face (as explained above) with the 'risk' those who currently write the tax bills face. Upon graduating from law school, where they were steeped in situational ethics, most Federal office holders went straight into guaranteed wages in government service or into a wealthy law firm where they were groomed for political office. Nowhere in their entire careers have they had to produce anything of material value--the direct opposite of almost every new private business. Once in political office, their salaries are guaranteed by the force of law, unlike those of the private business owners who must continuously struggle to collect the money owed them.

If private citizens don't pay what they are told to pay by these same lawmakers, Federal Marshals simply seize their property. People who get mad at the I.R.S. should realize that this arm of the government is just doing what it has been instructed to do by the majority of the five hundred and forty-five lawmakers in power. Once Americans create National Democracy and are therefore sovereign, the IRS will be governed by the laws passed by the majority and will conduct its affairs accordingly.

Neither the lawyers in government who are making the tax laws nor government employees know the meaning of risk. If they or their children get sick the tax payers pay all their medical bills. The lawmakers especially live like royalty off of the wealth created by others. Some have as many as three pensions funded at tax payers expense. None but a handful of the five hundred and forty-five have any notion of life the way the other two hundred sixty million citizens have to live it.

After the majority establishes a Democracy, the citizens will vote to approve all items including the level of compensation for their representatives. In the chapter titled 'Productive vs. Non Productive', I suggest a formula.

OPPORTUNITY COST

'Invest in America!'

Candidate Bill Clinton

To create a Democracy, the majority of Americans are going to have to put fear and confusion aside and start thinking again. To help you start, here is a test: (You'll have to do some research and calculations.) First, add up all the *investments* (taxes) that the five hundred and forty-five lawmakers are projected to withhold from the average U.S. paycheck and then spend over the next twenty years. Second, use the rate of annual increase in Federal *investments* (taxes) over the past ten years. Third, add this number together with the other one hundred million Americans who are working at paid jobs. Fourth, project the future value of those dollars if they were instead professionally invested directly (annually for the next twenty years) in growth stocks based upon an average annual growth rate for the last decade (I used 15%).

You should discover that in twenty years the amount of wealth in real value would be over one million dollars for every man, women and child who will then be living. (U.S. Population estimate in 2013 of three hundred million).

That's what it's going to cost each of you, your spouse, each of your children, your grandchildren, your parents, your brother and sisters, each of your friends and co-workers, every person you know plus every person who will be born in the U.S. in the next twenty years plus every new immigrant to keep the Federal Republic going.

Think of it. A million dollars in real purchasing power to spend in addition to anything you can accumulate on your own between now and then for every American then alive. That's what your opportunity cost is of keeping the Federal Republic.

Is listening to the galling lies and the divisive rhetoric of the five hundred and forty-five so enthralling? Are they worth it? Obviously the answer is no. Now that Democracy is possible it is inevitable. Act now to replace the Federal Republic with a National Democracy.

IMMIGRATION

Once American citizens are sovereign the majority of voters can decide the terms and conditions of immigration into the United States through National Referendum. They might also order the Army to do something practical like patrol the borders to prevent illegal entry into the country.

CAN THE BLIND LEAD THE BLIND?

'The problem is the people just don't understand my plans for America.'

President Bill Clinton -- June 1993.

*'You're stuck with me.
There's nothing you can do about it!'*

President Bill Clinton as quoted by Henry Gay
Seattle Post-Intelligencer   July 22, 1993.

'I never said that.'

President Bill Clinton -- on various occasions.

*'How can you deal with men who have no honor
except to remove them from power if you can?'*

The Author

Can The Blind Lead The Blind?

In the Fall of 1992, the largest newspaper in Arkansas, Bill Clinton's home state, urged Americans not to vote for him for President. To paraphrase the editors, its not that they were afraid Bill Clinton would violate his principles. It was that they were afraid he had no principles in the first place. Now the Nation and the entire world knows exactly what the editors were talking about. As this book goes to press the Justice Department has just ordered an investigation into the Whitewater Development affair.

Bill Clinton was elected President in November 1992 defeating George Bush and Ross Perot in the general election. But, even though he received 43% of the popular vote cast, his margin of victory represented less that 22% of the citizens who were entitled to vote by age. This means that approximately 78% of the Americans who could vote did not vote for Bill Clinton! In the year he has been President he has proven to the world that he is the personification of everything that defines what is wrong with the Federal Republic and with the majority of the other five hundred forty-four lawmakers who are sovereign with him over the Nation.

Tragically, it's a cliche to say that Mr. Clinton has embraced wholesale the failed policies of the past. And he's adding his own new formulas for wholesale failure for the future. The comedian Jay Leno recently said that the members of at least one tribe of Native Americans were publicly addressing Mr. Clinton by his native name, 'Broken Promises'. But how even Mr. Clinton's forked tongue can utter such profound falsehoods is beyond my imagination. His antics belong in comics such as 'Calvin and Hobbes' or 'Outland'.

If Mr. Clinton changed his name to 'Lotto Man' it would make more sense to me. I think all his speeches should be prefaced and concluded with the disclaimer that the average citizen has about the same odds of coming out ahead with Mr. Clinton as President as they do of winning the lottery. Those who serve him in the Congress and Federal bureaucracy could be, 'Latte Men or Women'.

On June 1, 1993 Bill Clinton was in Milwaukee, Wisconsin, campaigning for President seven months after the election (somebody forgot to tell him he won). He said he was trying to do something to change the 'brain dead' politics in Washington D.C. referring, of course, to those of George Bush and Ronald Reagan.

In the introduction to this book I stated that this was a work of conclusions. I wish Mr. Clinton a very long, peaceful, prosperous and happy life. But I have concluded that if Bill Clinton had any honor he would, along with his wife, the Vice President and entire Cabinet resign from office immediately.

If I have one thing for which to be grateful to Bill Clinton, it's that his lack of wise leadership combined with his lack of ability to speak honestly will motivate Americans to demand a National Democracy by the next presidential election in 1996. I expect the final lineup to be Bill Clinton, Ross Perot, and whoever the Republicans select. For now the speculation is almost pointless. What I do know is that it will be a race to see if the Republicans will beat Ross Perot to the punch of putting National Democracy forward as the main issue.

The News Media aligned with Clinton during the election and are again fawning over him and his entire federally-funded armada of anti-democracy legions to promote his socialist health care program. Nevertheless, when it fails, not even Clinton will be able to sidestep the only real issue of the 1996 campaign. Mr. Clinton will be against changing the Republic to a Democracy for all the reasons I have given in this book. But anything is possible. He has proven to the world he will say anything his financial contributors want to hear.

The only other possible way for Mr. Clinton to redeem his honor would be to demand of Congress an Amendment as outlined in this book without the usual lies and trickery and self-serving conditions. And then he should step aside and let Americans select a new President to help them rule their own nation. If this happens, it would be a miracle.

If Mr. Clinton does give lip service to Democracy the real question will be, will he and his Party step aside as the two hundred sixty million other citizens vote to replace the Federal Republic with a National Democracy? I'm afraid the answer is, with Mr. Clinton in the White House, they won't. The Democrats will find a way to delay forever. It will take a new President, someone who has the capacity to recognize and is devoted to the truth and Democracy.

Do we really want a proven liar (Clinton) to be the first President of the National Democracy? I don't recommend Ross Perot, but even he is honest enough to admit that he became rich through 'cost plus' government contracts. Compare George Washington, Thomas Jefferson or Abraham Lincoln to Bill Clinton. The image is enough to make any thinking person ill.

Mr. Clinton and the Democrats in Congress would want to tack on all kinds of additional amendments to placate their government legions and anti-Democracy minions exactly like their pro-communist counterparts in the Russian Parliament that Boris N. Yeltsin dismissed in September 1993. But, once the citizens are sovereign, final approval or disapproval of all legislation would belong to the will of the majority of voters, not to Bill Clinton or any other politician's financial supporters.

Even if Mr. Clinton were inclined to ask for the Constitutional Amendment unaltered, which I doubt, he would have no incentive to get it passed. In addition to that, even if he were so inclined, to date, Mr. Clinton hasn't even gotten his own Party to pass a single piece of wealth creating legislation. All he and his party have agreed to do is raise taxes again and borrow even more money and socialize another major industry (health care). What a complete surprise that must be for everyone.

In closing, I can just imagine that when the Democracy issue becomes the dominate theme of the 1996 election, Bill Clinton will declare, 'This is what I've been talking about all along. I said you didn't understand my plans for America!' Expect to hear any lie. This much is certain: Americans will soon elect in unprecedented numbers a new president who will be the last president of the Federal Republic and the first president of the National Democracy. An amendment similar if not identical to the one I propose in the first part of this book will be passed. Americans will be sovereign at last.

But no matter what happens, in the end the citizens of our Nation will be sovereign. Neither Bill Clinton and his hordes nor any other collusion of anti-Democracy power brokers can stop it.

CHAMPIONS?

'So they counted out for him thirty silver coins.'

Matthew 26:15 -- Referring to Judas Iscariot

Immediately after leaving office, Ronald Reagan left for Japan where he received millions of dollars in cash from Japanese businessmen. This payment was said to be a gift but it had every appearance of being a payment for arranging the transfer of control over much of American industry and real estate into their hands in exchange for their tacit agreement to loan trillions to the U.S. Government to pay government employees to produce nothing. The Act still stands along with the revelation that Mr. Reagan and his wife were guided on a daily basis by an astrologer as the most tragic repudiations of what he claimed he stood for. After Democracy is realized, the citizens will have the sovereign right to demand an accounting.

It may seem absurd to you that I would hold Ronald Reagan accountable for these acts. But he promised so much and delivered so little. Whatever intentions he may have had upon becoming President, Ronald Reagan quickly drowned in the quagmire of taxes, Japanese special interests and weapons industry lobbyists.

It is self-evident that the five hundred and forty-five lawmakers who rule the United States of America cannot do the thinking for the other two hundred sixty million Americans. When the citizens of the United States of American are finally sovereign, their collective wisdom shall reign supreme.

In 1979 I moved back into the City of Seattle. In the Spring of 1980 I officially joined the Republican Party and became a precinct committeeman for my Central District Seattle neighborhood. They told me at the County Convention that I was the first Republican precinct committee representative from that district in thirty years. I became a George Bush delegate to the County convention but was aced out by the Reagan fanatics.

After the National Convention I joined the campaign for Reagan and got to meet him along with all the other workers when he came to Seattle before the election. (I also got to see both Jimmy Carter and John Anderson that summer.) The rest of the story regarding the election is history.

In 1984, during Reagan's re-election campaign, I organized a protest group of twenty stockbrokers and businessmen plus my mother to attend an outdoor Walter Mondale rally in downtown Seattle. Two weeks before, the news media had devoted half of the coverage of a Reagan visit to Seattle by featuring three anti-Reagan lesbian protestors. I decided to try a similar tactic on Mondale.

At the rally there were, I estimate, over twenty thousand Mondale supporters in attendance. Our plan was simple. We stood with our Ronald Reagan signs without saying a word in the middle of the crowd until the newspaper and television cameras showed up.

As the thousands surrounding us jeered and kicked at us, the news media recorded my statement of protest. We captured about a third of the local and national television coverage as well as that of the local newspapers. It was great! Reagan didn't need any help to win that election but I felt great satisfaction nevertheless.

But in spite of his overwhelming mandate from the voters, Ronald Reagan failed as a President for one reason: He engaged the other five hundred forty-four lawmakers on their terms. I doubt it ever occurred to him to lead the cause to amend the Constitution to change the United States from a Federal Republic to a National Democracy. And in failing to seize the opportunity for meaningful and permanent change he became part of the problem.

In the 1960's John Kennedy attacked the U.S. steel industry solely for political reasons to divide the country and to take the attention off his own failures. In the 1970's, Nixon, Ford and Carter all attacked the auto and oil industries. In the 1980's Reagan and Bush attached the manufacturing industry in general by abandoning it under the guise of being 'non-competitive'. Our *'champions'* have scuttled each of these domestic industries to take public attention off of their own lies and failures. And for what result? To borrow money to pay people to produce nothing in exchange for their vote and campaign activities.

So far in the 1990's, Bill and Hillory Clinton's target is the medical industry. Don't plan on getting sick.

Champions?

If we don't act soon, the next U.S. industry that will be destroyed by tomorrow's 'champion' will most likely be the computer industry. You the citizens need to become your own champions. It's time to intervene by changing the Federal Republic to a National Democracy.

LACK OF CHARACTER

*"Americans deserve better lawmakers than those
who can only tell the truth by accident."*

The Author

The law schools in America have one thing in common: They teach situational ethics. Under this system of thought any statement or evidence that enhances your client's position and diminishes his adversary is good. Any statement or evidence that diminishes your client's position and enhances his adversary is bad. An attorney may withhold or ignore information as long as the client pays. Truth doesn't matter. The ends justify the means. A lawyer's compensation is specifically dependant upon mastering this outlook. The better skilled they are at it, the more income they receive.

To a sociopathic liar, any words or actions which enhance one's own position is good. Any words or actions which diminish one's own position is bad. What separates sociopathic liars from the rest of humanity is that they believe their own lies, even if it contradicts what they said only hours or days ago. They can be very confusing and cause great havoc around them, especially when they have power and a most honorable title such as Governor, Congressman, Senator, or President.

Mr. Clinton's January 1994 State of the Union speech could become a text book example of what such a mind is capable of. The chasm between his 'truth' and reality for Americans is ever widening. For instance, neither he nor the majority of the federal republicans who rule with him have reduced the deficit by *one penny* nor do they have any plans to do so in the future. They haven't cut spending at all! All they've done is slow down the projected baseline increases. (see balanced budget). That's what Mr. Clinton called 'cutting the deficit'. The hypocrisy and out right lies so gleefully delivered by Mr. Clinton in his speech were enough to make any thinking person vomit. Robert Dole's analysis after the speech pointed out at least a few the President's contradictions and falsehoods. Thank God there are at least some elected American leaders with honor.

Americans are not being fooled. We have also noticed that the most promiscuous men in power are the biggest advocates of feminist rights. Why? Do such men really believe what they are advocating? Hardly. (You know their names.) They don't want to be held responsible for what they themselves have done.

The House banking scandal or the House post office scandal, if they occurred instead in the financial industry, would have resulted in expulsion, fines and/or imprisonment for the offenders. But because they happened within the center of power itself, the members of the House of Representatives are not accountable for the laws they break because they are sovereign. After the fact, the House leaders invented a convenient lie to excuse the banking fraud, and they are trying to simply pretend that the post office scandal never happened. Even Richard Nixon was given two years to voluntarily resign after his crimes relating to Watergate were exposed. He remains an unindicted co-conspirator but, you would have to be a historian of the Congress to name even one member of the five hundred and forty-five who's ever been kicked out and imprisoned.

Character does matter. Before the 1992 Presidential election, the largest newspaper in Arkansas printed a full page editorial regarding Bill Clinton, their Governor of twelve years. To paraphrase them, the editors said they weren't concerned that Mr. Clinton would compromise his principles once he was President. Their real concern was that he had no principles in the first place. After Democracy, those obviously lacking in integrity will be recalled in short order.

Beyond the immediate and obvious concern over the President's lack of control and inability to speak truthfully much less recognize it, there are larger issues. It is self-evident that, at least the majority of the five hundred and forty-five, don't want the public, starting with school children, to be taught that there is such a thing as absolute morality. It's self-evident that the officials themselves don't want to be held accountable for what they have done. Under National Democracy, character will be of paramount importance even if it no longer has value under the Federal Republic. The citizens of the United States already know exactly what to do. After you create Democracy you will finally be empowered to do it.

LEADERSHIP

*'For lack of leadership a nation falls,
but many advisors make victory sure.'*

Proverbs 11:14

George Bush was one of the most qualified presidents of our Federal Republic. In my lifetime, his achievements, especially in the area of foreign policy, eclipse those of all other leaders who have held the office, although Mr. Nixon's trip to China also deserves an honorable mention. Mr. Bush's ability to disarm situations potentially dangerous to the United States and our Allies is unmatched.

Mr. Bush's personal example of honest, open and skillful leadership was clouded by the fact that Bill Clinton, with Ross Perot's able engineering, was able to unseat him in the 1992 general election. I believe Mr. Perot's aim for the White House has always been 1996 where he has jockeyed all along to face the weakest of all possible opponents, meaning of course, Bill Clinton.

In American political history, whenever three national parties have run viable candidates, the two strongest candidates have split the vote allowing the weakest and poorest choice through the door. If not for Ross Perot, our President today would certainly be George Bush.

Mr. Bush tried harder and showed greater skill and willingness, much more so than any other President of this age, to solicit the cooperation of the other five hundred forty-four who make the laws. He stood alone as an example to the rest of the lawmakers as a reminder of their duty to the American people. George Bush and Dan Quayle understood as well as anyone that there can be no true freedom in a Nation not rooted firmly in Christian principles. It is axiomatic.

Mr. Bush served his country honorably during a time of war and during peace. Even so, who among even his most ardent supporters could say that George Bush was completely able to direct the affairs the Nation any more than any of the other five hundred forty-four lawmakers who ruled the nation with him? He was only one person. It was said by his critics that he had no domestic agenda for America. This was simply not true. As President, Mr. Bush was out maneuvered in Congress by superior numbers on every domestic issue and then blamed for his inability to override the Democrats' own agenda.

To his fault, President Bush continued placating the Democrats through the policy of the previous eight years of transferring wealth away from Americans to Asia and other nations under the guise of 'Global Competivness' so in turn the U.S. Government could borrow more money from the same countries to pay non-productive labor at home.

The Democrats in Congress responded to President Bush's leadership in their normal way. With an absolute promise to cut spending, they persuaded Mr. Bush to recant his 'Read my lips. No new taxes,' pledge. In 1990 the Democrats betrayed their own agreement to cut spending with George Bush and then blamed him for the downturn in the economy which came about because of their own normal practices of tax, borrow and spend.

George Bush used the incident which became the Persian Gulf War to take American's mind off his abandonment of his 'no new taxes' pledge and the faltering economy. In the end, the Gulf war became another military adventure where America failed to vanquish the enemy (meaning of course, Saddam Hussein). Nevertheless, there were times during the 1992 Presidential Campaign when people would ask me who I was going to vote for? Bush, Perot or Clinton? I would answer, 'I may be frustrated with some of the things President Bush has done, but I haven't gone insane. Of course I'm voting for George Bush.' But with the likes of Bill Clinton being elected to the Nation's highest office, it is obvious that we don't only need a new president but a new government.

It is extremely presumptuous of me to suggest that I know what Mr. Bush would say about the conclusions I've recorded in this book. Perhaps he would disagree with all of them. But I suspect in his heart, Mr. Bush might at least agree that we the citizens, the two hundred sixty millions who are not yet in power, must put aside the divisions of the past as well as the majority of the leaders of the past. We must also press on to the one and only solution: National

Democracy. We must produce our own new uncompromisable leaders.

The citizens of the United States of America must learn to make laws through initiative. We must learn to set the rates and conditions of our own taxes and other laws by voting to confirm or deny what the five hundred and forty-five lawmakers recommend. That we must begin to get used to ruling ourselves and choosing new pro-Democracy leaders is unquestionably our first challenge. Our next task will be demand that they amend the Constitution, changing the Republic to Democracy. It is self-evident that five hundred and forty-five lawmakers cannot do the thinking for the rest of the two hundred sixty million Americans. There can be no delay of Democracy if we are going to have a Nation at all.

POLITICS AS USUAL?

*'It is for freedom
that Christ has set us free.
Stand firm and do not let yourselves
be burdened again
by a yoke of slavery.'*

The Apostle Paul

Galatians 5.1

The five hundred and forty-five lawmakers who are sovereign over our Nation say that only they can protect your rights and freedom. Then they proceed to whip up groups against one another, through racial, economic and sexual division to maintain control. They employ the same anti-Democracy arguments the Soviet Communist Party used to justify its concentration of power-with nearly the same results: Totalitarian rule.

The determinant factors between the United States and the ex-Soviet Union are that the U.S. citizens still have some private property rights, and limited freedom of speech and travel. But the five hundred and forty-five U.S. lawmakers aren't any less powerful than were their Soviet counterparts.

Our leaders don't have any more insight, nor are they less corrupt. The Communists believed that only a small elite group could defend the rights of the Soviet citizens, exactly as do their U.S. counterparts. That the United States built a trillion dollars worth of nuclear weapons didn't change the Soviet Union into a Republic. The Russian people themselves decided that they didn't need defending at the price they were being charged. Neither should we accept what we are being offered.

The divisions in this country exist because we are being deliberately pitted against one another by the majority of the five hundred and forty-five lawmakers in Washington D.C. to take our attention off of the one and only real issue: We need Democracy now.

Of course you can expect that many of the Republicans currently in power and all but a handful of the Democrats will resist Democracy. They can only exist as power brokers in a Republic. They and all other existing political parties and movements including, 'United We Stand, America, Inc.' can only exist as they are by dividing Americans. The formula is old. So far, 'Divide and Conquer' has served Ross Perot well in his 1996 bid for the White House: Bill Clinton will be Perot's straw man.

After Democracy, U.S. Senators and Congressmen should be required to live and work in their home states and districts. They should be forbidden to take contributions from any source other than from the individual citizens of their own district.

The majority of the five hundred and forty-five lawmakers in Washington D.C. and their Civil Service legions of non-productive labor cannot control the rest of the two hundred sixty million Americans if we don't cooperate with them. We must refuse to be divided on the issue of Democracy. We must peacefully refuse to settle for anything less, whatever the cost. This may be our one and only chance.

SUPREME COURT

*'The period of human history when a handful of
sovereign individuals can dictate the fate of hundreds of
millions of other people is coming to an end.'*

The Author

Once you the citizens are sovereign you should not only
subject Supreme Court nominees to voter confirmation but to recall
as well. There is no evidence to support the claim that by giving
Justices lifetime employment that somehow their objectivity is
guaranteed. In fact, exactly the opposite is true. As things stand now
the Justices are nothing more than lawyers who have become political
agents for whichever political party controls the Senate.

Many of the current problems in the Federal Republic of the
United States began forty-five years ago when this group of nine
lawyers, lead by Justice Hugo Black, started creating their own laws
and issuing orders instead of passing judgments over individual cases.

The point is not whether or not some of the social directives
needed to be carried out, rather that the Supreme Court was not
created for that purpose. Since the Democrats in Congress and some
of the Justices disagree with the original purpose of the Supreme
Court the Judicial system itself must be changed by the voters as you
take sovereignty over the entire government as outlined in the first
part of this book.

Under National Democracy the majority of the citizens will
have the sovereign right to confirm or deny each and every
Constitutional ruling of the Supreme Court. If the citizens make
mistakes they will soon recognize it and have the power to correct it.

It's worth noting that the most recent appointment to the
Supreme Court, Justice Ruth Ginsburg, testified in her Senate
confirmation hearings that she apparently agrees with those who
believe that the High Court possessed the right and even the
obligation to make rulings that effect political policy. Not only did

she agree with the Feminist's ideology of abortion on demand as a First Amendment right, she also stated that she was a strong advocate of ending gender discrimination. Her use of the word 'gender' instead of 'sex' confused some of the news reporters I listened to on the radio. They dismissed her choice of words as not being relevant.

What the reporters failed to understand is that within the lesbian and homosexual community, using gender instead of sex is a 'code' word. Lesbians and homosexuals are promoting the notion that instead of two genders, male and female, there are four and possibly even more distinct genders. Heterosexual females are considered one gender. Heterosexual males are the second. Lesbians are the third gender and homosexuals are the fourth. Such profoundly confused reasoning leaves the door open for any number of genders. If they succeed, gender as defined by the lesbians and homosexuals will become the universal basis for affirmative action. (It's already being used in several municipal and state governments.) It may someday be a Federal offence for you to encourage your son or daughter to grow up to be heterosexual or even to offer them advice on the subject. It would be considered a hate crime. Stranger things have happened in totalitarian governments to which any survivor of the Chinese Cultural Revolution can attest.

The question you should be asking is 'Does Justice Ginsburg agree with the homosexual and lesbian definition of gender as outlined above?' If she doesn't, will she deny such agreement and be willing to publicly clarify her own definition? (She and all the other Justices will have to be reconfirmed by the voters under National Democracy.) If even one Supreme Court Justice believed in ending gender discrimination (as the lesbians and homosexuals define it) and who had every intention of acting upon such confused nonsense in future rulings, this would singularly be a justification for Americans to change the government from a Federal Republic to a National Democracy.

Once the citizens are sovereign the majority can remove any Federal official from any position of authority for any reason in any general election including Supreme Court Justices (no confidence vote). The wisdom of the majority of citizens will not only make, confirm or deny every law, ruling or tax but such decisions will be Constitutional by definition.

REPUBLICANS

Whatever political freedoms and individual liberties that American citizens still enjoy in the close of the twentieth century, they owe much to a small group of courageous individuals within the Republican Party.

No more than a few dozen of the elected Republican officials in two of the three branches of the U.S. Federal Government have been the only force standing between the rest of the five hundred odd lawmakers and their insatiable and unthinking lust for power.

Guided by their selfless service to the Christian principles of Democracy and encouraged by the rank and file of Republican party members, these heroes have stood directly in the way of their fellow lawmaker's efforts to change our nation into a totalitarian society.

It has taken all the effort and concentration that these patriots could muster to slow down their opponent's lockstep efforts. The entire Federal bureaucracy, including the Civil Service, is controlled by the Democrat party lawmakers. It is in fact nothing more than a political arm of the party that is actually being paid to help trick the rest of us by whatever means into voting for their anti-Democracy anti-Christian programs. Unfortunately, the few pro-Democracy Republicans have been losing the battle to stop the anti-Democracy forces inch by inch. After forty years of struggle, they are close to being routed.

They have been hindered and defamed by the majority of the five hundred forty-five lawmakers, but many of the setbacks have been aided and abetted by members of their own Republican party. Yet, I believe that it is from among these few dozen courageous men and women Republicans, plus at most a handful of the newly elected Democrats (who act independently) that will come the American leadership to change our Nation from a Federal Republic to a National Democracy.

The Republicans have not been without major contributors to the march toward totalitarian rule. Ronald Reagan was elected in 1980 declaring that 'Government is the problem'. Instead of taking the necessary steps to really change anything (meaning the government itself) Reagan tried to take on the other five hundred forty-four lawyers but on their terms. You may be asking, what else was he suppose to do? The only thing that matters is that he failed.

President Reagan was perceived to have a few early victories in the area of reducing taxes but he was dealing with symptoms of the problem, not the cause. He was beaten by the system itself. It is true that the federal income tax rates were lowered by agreement of the majority in Congress but almost all the deductions were eliminated and the Social Security taxes were raised substantially. The average person ended up paying much more in taxes, not less. The tax rates have since been raised substantially both in 1990 and again in 1993 but without the deductions added back on. One word that comes to mind to describe this situation is '*rape*'.

Ronald Reagan ended his two terms of office with accolades by the Republicans for his attempts but, because of his compromises with the tax-crazed majority in Congress, he left office with all but the wealthiest Americans in worse shape economically than they had been.

Reagan was also corrupted by his Office. After two terms, he disgraced himself and betrayed all United States citizens by flying to Japan to collect millions from the new billionaires he directly helped to create at the expense of the average American. Honoraria to former public officer holders appears as nothing other than a bribe paid after the fact.

Also, the disclosure at the close of his second term that both Ronald and Nancy Reagan used an astrologer to guide their every move came as quite a shock to Christians. The knowledge that we had been lied to for a decade (that Reagan was a Christian) still galls most of us. Yet it explains many things about the man and our own gullibility and vulnerability. We can not afford to be tricked again.

As I discussed in some depth in other chapters, all throughout the 1980's the majority of the five hundred and forty-five lawmakers in office, led by the Republicans, worked overtime to change the laws of our Nation to sell off our manufacturing base to the Asian bankers in exchange for loans which created unfathomable deficits.

What's worse is that the multi-trillions of dollars of borrowed money was paid to non-productive U.S. labor (government workers, welfare recipients and all other transfer payment recipients) for no other reason than to buy votes. While the Republicans championed nuclear weapons, the Democrats, as always, championed themselves. But both parties created the problems together.

However high-sounding the rhetoric, how does spending borrowed money to get politicians reelected compare with the citizen's responsibility for having to repay the loans?   Global economics was just a narrow field of academic study for people like me before the phrase was foisted down the economic throats of American citizens as an excuse to borrow more money. (See chapters on 'American Economy Reborn'.)

Richard Nixon was elected in 1968 on the campaign promise that he had a secret plan to end the war in Vietnam. His 'peace with honor' plan became 'war with horror'. It was just the beginning of his many lies. Then, after professing to being an advocate of Monetary Policy all his life, he directed the Texas Democrat John Connaly (a Lyndon Johnson protege) to impose wage and price controls, but only because wage and price controls were to be the Democrats' main political issue in the upcoming 1972 Presidential Elections. With the Watergate cover-up, and his scheming in general, Nixon's public record of lies ranks right up there with any whoppers Bill Clinton has told or is ever likely to tell.

Mr. Nixon torpedoed NASA's space budget for no other reason than that it was a pet project of Lyndon Johnson's. Nixon was a profound failure in so many ways, it's difficult to know where to begin listing them. About the only area that Mr. Nixon is thought to have excelled in is foreign policy and only with China. He reopened diplomatic and trade relations with the communist nation with a State visit and by granting them trading partner status. It was hailed as a profound accomplishment at the time. In retrospect, perhaps if Mr. Nixon hadn't accepted China on its own terms, China might now be a Republic as are all the other formerly communist nations of Europe and central Asia. In the balance, Mr. Nixon's lies and crimes against our Nation place him as one of the worst Presidents in American history eclipsed only by that of his predecessor in office, Lyndon Johnson.

In defense of at least some of the Republicans I have to say objectively that, based upon recent events, the citizens can measure at least a degree of integrity within the Republican Party (compared to the Democrat Party). The House of Representatives' banking scandal last year showed that the vast numbers of the illegal banking activities were being committed primarily by Democrats, not Republicans. The decision to ignore the crimes was made entirely by the Democrats in the House as voiced by their Speaker Thomas

Foley.   The same thing is now happening in the House of Representatives post office scandal with Dan Rostenkowski. If either crime had happened in any other place but under the direct control of the five hundred and forty-five lawmakers in power, Federal Marshals would have immediately been sent in to arrest them all. All records would have already been confiscated and the trial dates would have been set. Prison would be on the horizon for all of them if for no other reason than for conspiring together to cover up the crimes.

Overall I have to give the Republicans failing grades. The primary reason is that to date, they have failed to recognize that the only way to deal with the real problems of our nation is to change the government from a Federal Republic to a National Democracy and let the citizens vote on every issue, item-by-item.

It is self-evident that five hundred and forty-five lawmakers who rule our nation cannot do the thinking for the other two hundred sixty million Americans. Why haven't the Republicans already acted to change the government to Democracy?

But as I have said above, I have high hopes for some of them as advocates of National Democracy.   I believe that it will be primarily from this group that the core leadership will come to change the U.S. government to a Democracy.

DEMOCRATS

'Patriots don't divide the country. They unite it.'

Bill Clinton speaking at the
Vietnam memorial on Memorial Day in 1993.

It's ironic that Bill Clinton, a living symbol of falsehoods, self-delusion, betrayal and division should utter the words quoted above. Obviously his speech writers came up with the phrase as an attempt to schmooze the Vietnam veterans. They naturally resent Mr. Clinton's alleged anti-American activities during the war. If he believed his words, Mr. Clinton would prove it by immediately resigning from office.

Next to the thought of the impending change from the Federal Republic to a National Democracy, there is probably nothing that frightens the Democrats in Washington D.C. more that the thought of one of their own in the White House.

Bill Clinton won the White House without the full and active support of even one single nationally prominent Democrat. It wasn't just that the Democrat office holders didn't want Bill Clinton to win. They didn't want any Democrat to win.

Why should they? If you're an elected Democrat in Washington D.C., you already know the answer. The Democrats have controlled the House of Representatives and have been the majority in Congress overall for 40 years. That's where were all the spending bills originate. They've controlled the Senate for 36 years. The Republican Presidents haven't selected anyone for the Supreme Court, Department Heads or even their own Cabinet that the Democrats haven't had final confirmation over. By their own lack of action, the Democrats know they are immune from prosecution no matter what crimes they commit against the American people.

For four decades, the Democrats have been able to pass every single bit of spending and social legislation they wanted all the while blaming the results of their failures and the inflation and deficits on the Republican Presidents, current or past.

Based upon the recorded facts of history of the last half of this century, with a Republican in the White House, the Democrats in majority in Congress have obtained anything they wanted yet at the same time shifted all the public blame to the Republican President. The unparalleled amount they've simply looted from Americans is eclipsed only by their unparalleled group and individual hypocrisy. Those now in office are the greatest thieves measured in total wealth stolen of any ruling body in any time period in human history. By your own inaction they are legally able to get away with it.

The Democrats say they want to undo the damage done by Reagan and Bush. Under Democrat control from 1981 through 1992, the House budget rose from approximately five hundred billion to one and a third trillion. Every penny of taxes spent and every penny of money borrowed was initiated and first approved by and for the Democrats in control of the House. The Democrats in the House of Representatives have controlled spending from beginning to end for the past forty years (spending bills must originate in the House). Any one who denies this is either lying, 'brain dead' (Mr. Clinton's own words), or unconscious. And still it wasn't enough, so they borrowed money as I've already discussed.

Today the deficit stands at four trillion dollars. That's $4,000,000,000,000 they've borrowed and have already spent by signing in your name. Even with the official Federal govenment's own most optimistic estimates, Mr. Clinton's tax and spend solution (passed August 1993) will add over $1,000,000,000,000 more to the deficit by 1999. You and your children owe it in addition to all the other taxes you will have to pay this year and every year as long as they remain sovereign. In the future if the five hundred and forty-five want to borrow and spend more than the tax revenues approved directly by the citizens they should be held personally liable to repay the debts.

It is ironic that the few hundred men and women who control the Legislative and Executive branches of U.S. government call themselves 'Democrats'. It is self-evident that as a body the Democrat office holders think and act more than any group or ideology and practice as did their political counterparts in the ex-Soviet Union. They don't mind at all if you understand who and what they are as long as you don't do anything about it.

In Europe and Asia the totalitarian governments have failed utterly to live up to their own communist ideals. The socialist economic models necessary for Communist governments to maintain power have enslaved those citizens. Attempts at that form of government have been thoroughly discredited everywhere but in the United States and with the lawmakers of the Democrat Party.

Those who voted for Bill Clinton and those who now still support him are suffering from a group hallucination brought on by decades of their failure to fulfil even one promise of Democracy through government spending and social thought control. Based upon their results, they are unwilling to think or reason about anything other than transferring more power to themselves. They are worse than drug addicts in the last stages of addiction before death.

That there are citizens who don't work for the government or who are not direct beneficiaries of transfer payments who still vote for Democrat office holders or who even have kind things to say about them is a testimony to the narcotic-like grip that their group hallucination has on Americans.

The Democrat office holders as a group define the anti-Democracy and therefore anti-Christian movement in America. The Democrat's plan remains what it has been for thirty years. Destroy more capital industries with higher taxes to pay more nonproductive labor to insure they can continue the cycle. To do this they must continue to prevent any philosophy of true freedom, equality, thrift, honesty and virtue, all uniquely Christian principles from being communicated. At the same time they claim to be the champions of good intentions. The road to bankruptcy is paved with their intentions. Anyone who can reason is their enemy. What they all share in common is that they haven't the wisdom either to know or understand what they have done and where they are dragging the Nation.

In my lifetime everything the Democrat office holders have tried has failed to produce capital for the Nation. Every ideological move against Christianity has brought more lawlessness and violence and immorality manifested in the ever-rising rate of illegitimate children, abortion, crime, sexually transmitted diseases, gangs, murders, corruption, national debt and has brought totally confused groups such as lesbians and homosexuals into authority positions at the highest levels of power in all levels of Federal, State and Local governments.

It used to make me boiling angry to watch politicians smile as they told lie after lie after lie after lie when it was perfectly obvious that they and everyone else knew they were lying. It took decades for me to realize that most of them cannot tell truth from fiction. And this because they are lawyers trained in situational ethics as I discuss in the chapter on lawyers. That's when it became obvious to me that it was necessary to write this book about creating a new government.

There is a certain sad logic to explain why the citizens of the Nation who see the same problems I do keep reelecting Democrats to Congress. In human society leadership is scarce and wise leadership is even more scarce. Humans are so desperate for leadership that they will follow anyone who exhibits that quality to the extent that a person displays it, however irrational the message may be. Take the citizens from Spokane, Washington, the home district of House Speaker Thomas Foley. The Democrats have outright control of the House, Senate and now the White House. They reward only according to Party lines and give extra bonuses to districts whose members cooperate.

Under the current seniority system, the only way underpopulated states can get tax money back from the Federal Government is for citizens in small communities to compromise. Americans hold their noses in the voting booths and keep sending the 'compromise' back to Washington D.C. term after term in the hopes that one day their compromise will get seniority and be able to funnel some of the money back home. What other choice have the relatively powerless and hapless citizens had up until now? It's the same despaired mentality that drives people to purchase lottery tickets. But I put it to you that the price you're paying is too high. Do we have to wait until all our freedom is gone and the economy is completely destroyed like those in Eastern Europe before we act?

The politicians in office don't really care at all that half of those eligible to vote are too disgusted to participate. Their power is not diminished in any way as a consequence. That the citizens feel hopelessness and despair and stay home on voting day only enhances their power. But after the Republic is changed to Democracy the citizens will have a real choice at last as they will be sovereign.

In the 1992 Primary elections, the citizens of the State of Washington put a term limits initiative on the ballot. Thomas Foley campaigned around the State against the Initiative. He told the citizens that they had no right to set term limits no matter what law they passed.

Mr. Foley was instrumental in bringing large sums of money from out of our State to frighten the voters of Washington State with threats of the loss of water rights to California (the bogeyman). Can you imagine this in the Evergreen State? I think it has rained at least every other day this year where I live. This is my own joke of course (for outsiders) because Eastern Washington is nothing but a desert if not for the irrigation water from the Columbia River. Still, it's galling to be a witness to such avarice and contempt as Mr. Foley displays for the citizens of his own State.

In spite of Mr. Foley's efforts, a version of the Initiative still passed in the Fall general election. In June 1993, Mr. Foley, and the League of Women Voters (a national organization with lots of cash at Mr. Foley's beck & call) filed a lawsuit in Federal Court to overturn as unconstitutional the law that we the citizens passed. He'll probably succeed unless the U.S. citizens create Democracy before the case comes to trial. (In case you've missed the point, the game is rigged.)

Mr. Foley apparently craves power so much that he thinks he is above the will of the citizens of Washington. And judging from their words and actions most of the five hundred and forty-five think exactly the same. Under the current Republic they are, in fact, legally sovereign just as Mr. Foley maintains.

None of these issues will matter after Democracy but in the chapter on Attorneys, I do recommend that the citizens consider placing a moratorium upon permitting lawyers be Congressmen and Senators until a new generation of lawyers, not trained in situational ethics, graduates. The citizens must not only control the military but the law as well.

But Democracy has to begin somewhere. Let it be with you in your Congressional district. This year don't send your 'compromise' back to Washington D.C. Vote for someone new who promises only to deliver Democracy. Only on the day that the Constitution is amended will you become sovereign over the three branches of government.

ROSS PEROT

'If a man wants to buy a green suit,
turn on a green light.'

Marketing advice from master salesman, Paul Hoppes, Sr.

In the end, Ross Perot is merely trying to sell Americans
another compromise. But compromise is what we have now! The
word literally defines the Federal Republic. His book, 'Not For Sale
At Any Price' is full of useful information but it's worth noting that
most of the themes and facts are and have been the meat and drink of
the Republican Party's rank and file for decades. By all means
purchase it and study the material if you haven't already especially if
you are a Democrat.

I am grateful for Mr. Perot's compilation of the facts as I had
originally planned to include much of the same information and
graphs in this book. He's not the only businessman in America. But
Mr. Perot saved me some of the trouble and allowed me to go
straight to the conclusions.

Mr. Perot's book doesn't mention many of the factors that lead
up to the current situation. Perhaps he believes they are so obvious it
is unnecessary. If that's the case then in that sense I would agree with
him. In addition, he does present many economic facts but
unfortunately comes to the wrong conclusions. Ross Perot's so-called
solutions are really nothing but more plans to treat the symptoms of
bad government, not the cause. The citizens of the United States
have already had too much of that.

The root problem with our Nation is self evident: Five hundred
and forty-five lawmakers cannot do the thinking for the two hundred
sixty million other Americans. The one and only way out is to change
the Federal Republic to a National Democracy. The citizens need to
be sovereign over the three branches of government, exactly the
opposite of now. The voters must be sovereign and have the power of

referendum and the right to directly approve every law, every tax, every rule, item by item.

In his book, Mr. Perot doesn't mention the word Christian one time that I could find. As I have stated elsewhere and as is self-evident to anyone who can reason, Democratic principles cannot exist outside of a Christian society. It's failed everywhere its been tried in non-Christian countries (especially in Africa and Asia). The only exception is Japan where the United States has forced it upon the defeated population with atomic bombs. Even there, a few dozen families who own more than half of all the wealth of Japan largely ignore the elected government and conduct business however they want. That's the reason the United States companies can't penetrate their markets, in spite of the Japanese government's pretended cooperation.

To my knowledge, I've read all the published biographies published on Mr. Perot, including the one written by his paid employee. He made his multi-billion dollar fortune on cost-plus government contracts from various welfare agencies. No one denies it. He was better at getting money from the various state and federal government entities than all the rest. His great skill at influencing the tiny group of elected officials at the federal and state levels is now eclipsed only by his audacious request that you follow him or vote for him for President. But accepting Ross Perot as President to fix the problems with government spending, influence buying and special interests would be on the same parallel as hiring the most successful street gangster to be in charge of law enforcement.

In chapter four (Good People, Bad System) of his recent book, 'Not For Sale At Any Price' Mr. Perot confesses that he thinks the American people elect outstanding citizens to serve us in Washington. That one admission betrays everything else there is to know about Mr. Perot. He conveniently ignores the tragic reality that the majority of career politicians in Federal office are lawyers trained in situational ethics from their first days in law school. For them, it is obvious that if they ever knew the difference between truth and fiction they've long since discarded that knowledge as a minor inconvenience.

Mr. Perot's book is all about money and obviously he has studied monetary cost to the exclusion of all else. He is revealed in the above mentioned book more than in any other document. Everything is dollars and cents to him and you and I and all other

Americans are just another business opportunity that's passing him by.

Mr. Perot obviously sees himself in the White House some day and doesn't want to personally offend the five hundred and forty-five lawmakers.   If he really believes the five hundred and forty-five are outstanding citizens then he lacks the judgement to positively change things and his measure of wisdom is in serious question. After Bill Clinton, can America survive yet another federal republican?

Mr. Perot is a master salesman and a man of enormous power who with his words is offering to sell to Americans what he thinks we will buy. But we need to break ourselves of the feeling that we need one man or one women to champion our cause. With our trust firmly in God, as a Nation we must become our own champions. There is only one way to do this. We must peacefully and legally change our government from a Federal Republic to a National Democracy.

With his electronic town hall meetings, Mr. Perot wants to make the Republic more palatable, just like the rest of the five hundred and forty-five. He already has the taxpayer's money. Now he wants to exercise power over us. I say come to your senses and deny it to him and all of them before it's too late.

Mr. Perot's electronic town hall will still leave the five hundred and forty-five lawmakers sovereign. Public opinion polls have been telling the three branches of government what the citizens want for a century. It hasn't made any direct difference. Certainly not in the last thirty years. The politicians already know what the majority of Americans want. But they don't care. They know they don't have to. There is almost nothing we the citizens can do about their betrayal as long as the Republic continues.

Yet, imagine for a moment that Mr. Perot is elected in 1996. Even if a few members of his new party *(United We Stand, America, Inc. is actually a private corporation)* take seats in the Congress, he will be up against both the Democrats and Republicans in Congress. Unless the United We Stand, America, Inc., candidates sweep the elections, it's certain that nothing of what Mr. Perot wants will be passed.

Even with a temporary two-year majority in the Senate and a landslide victory, Ronald Reagan couldn't get things changed in the House. Reagan's struggles only gave the Democrats in majority a common focus as they shoved everything they wanted down the President's political throat. The only way Mr. Reagan could get the

Democrats to agree to lower the marginal tax rate was to agree to eliminate most of the tax deductions and let the Democrats in Congress borrow all the additional money they wanted to spend.

During the Reagan and Bush years the amount of Federal taxes collected annually increased threefold. The Democrats in charge of the House of Representatives where all the tax and spending bills originate were in tax Heaven as they had more tax money to spend than ever, plus all they could borrow. As a bonus, they had a Republican President on whom to place blame for all they were doing.

Ronald Reagan has been out of office for five years. The Democrats are still blaming *on him* their own social and economic atrocities that they themselves passed into law during Reagan's two terms. The same thing will happen to Mr. Perot unless he comes to power to amend the Constitution in favor of Democracy. And if he does, I predict he'll have to adjourn Congress to do it (see the chapter on passing the Amendment) because Congress would never pass it themselves with Perot as President.

But to view this pragmatically look at the trouble Mr. Clinton is having getting his own party to support his programs. Without pork barrel politics to buy votes few of his proposals would have made it through Congress. Even if I agreed that Ross Perot would make a good president, which I don't under his present platform, he won't have a chance to be effective as long as our government remains a Federal Republic. As I've said above, if Mr. Perot is elected, the Democrats and Republicans will concentrate on proving to the American people that the voters made a mistake. The other five hundred forty-four lawmakers will discount and dismiss Mr. Perot and his Party just as they have all other populist movements.

Under the Federal Republic, nothing Mr. Perot wants will ever make it out of committee. There will never be a vote, because his legislation will never make it to the floor of either legislative body. A voter mandate in itself won't help. In spite of Ronald Reagan's total political knockout of Walter Mondale in 1984, the Democrats in the House made it clear that it didn't matter and that they would pass only the legislation they wanted. And so it was.

But for this discussion, just suppose Mr. Perot is able to get a few key bills passed and proclaims victory for Americans. At best it will be a watered-down solution, a marginal improvement in only one area. He'll only be treating the symptoms. Congress makes the laws, not the President. In four years Ross Perot will be out of office and the citizens will still be left with the same need to change the government to a Democracy.

Ross Perot has stepped into a vacuum of leadership. I can't repeat it enough: Anyone who exhibits leadership will be followed to the extent he or she displays this quality no matter how irrational their message. Rational and wise leadership is the most scarce and precious quality on earth. American's can't settle for anything less. Especially not now.

Mr. Perot is dealing only with the symptoms of the root problem. To my knowledge he has never spoken out against abortion upon demand (or offered any alternatives as those in my chapter on abortion) and has made no stand against affirmative action for homosexuals. To my knowledge he's never repudiated the anti-Christian anti-Democracy revisionists in government and education who have succeeded in re-writing American history to exclude the beliefs of the Christians who founded the Nation.

Mr. Perot's apparent lack of wisdom, his own personal culpability in creating and assisting in the overburdening tax problems of the society and the fact that he apparently can't see the one and only answer precludes him from any real consideration for President. I've read the reports of how the local Perot volunteers are being treated with the strong-arm tactics from the Dallas headquarters of the United We Stand, America, Inc. I also wonder how a new party can expect to take hold with only one person making and voicing all the decisions? Can you name even one person other than Mr. Perot from his group? Mr. Perot's party seems to be the least democratic of any of the three major political parties.

My point here is that we don't need just a new President, Senator, Congressman or a Governor. We need a new government. We need a National Democracy. One in which the citizens are sovereign over the three branches of government. Besides personal character there is only one consideration for the next presidential candidate: Will the candidate deliver National Democracy according to the Amendments outlined in this book and then step aside and operate in an advisory capacity letting the citizens rule themselves?

After Ross Perot, the next version of Bill Clinton, Lyndon Johnson or Richard Nixon will be elected and will proclaim his own mandate to try to further destroy the social and economic fabric of society just like Mr. Clinton is doing now.

We need to change the government to a National Democracy so there will never be another Ross Perot or Bill Clinton, Richard Nixon, Lyndon Johnson or any of them to misdirect and loot the nation. The Congressmen, Senators and President we elect should serve us and not just in words. This requirement alone precludes all but a handful of those currently in office. Except for the President, the elected officials should live and work in their own communities where you can keep a daily eye on them so they will never forget to whom they are accountable.

Americans need a President who will officially yield final say over the government to you the citizens. A wise President who will be content to be an administrator, not a power broker (except for cases of national emergency where the President must direct the action). This leaves out Ross Perot.

I've said above and it's worth repeating again and again that Ross Perot, just like Bill Clinton or Ronald Reagan, has stepped into a vacuum. A vacuum where there is little or no clear thinking leadership. Instead, Americans need leaders with common sense (also known as wisdom).

Ross Perot's message to the United States is what Mikhail Gorbachev's message was to the Soviet Union. Mr. Gorbachev wanted to make Communism more palatable. When republican elections were held in the Soviet Union, Gorbachev became obsolete, superfluous. National Democracy will do the same thing to Ross Perot and most of the rest of the federal republicans now in office.

Americans should respond to Ross Perot by using language he'll understand: With Democracy we can cut out the middle man. We don't need you nor can we afford to have another federal republican as President.

AMERICANS

'...that we here highly resolve that these dead
shall not have died in vain, that this nation,
under God, shall have a new birth of freedom
and that government of the people,
by the people, for the people,
shall not perish from the earth.

From Abraham Lincoln's Address at Gettysburg in
1863

From the perspective of the majority of the five hundred and forty-five lawmakers who rule our Nation, it is to their advantage for Americans to feel too helpless and powerless to do anything about the situation those in government have deliberately created. In the last thirty years the numbers of eligible citizens who refuse to vote has grown to more than half of the adult population.

The non-voters I know are glibly apathetic on the surface but inside they are boiling in disgusted and impotent fury. None of the candidates of any of the three political parties represents what they want. The five hundred and forty-five depend upon their ongoing and ever-increasing ability to pit men against women, Blacks against Whites, Asians against Blacks and Hispanics, Christians against Jews, Christians against other Christians, old against the young and of course those above the poverty line against those below to keep themselves sovereign.

It's interesting to note, but not in any way is it unusual, that for all the pretense of championing the 'downtrodden', apparently 70% of Bill Clinton's Cabinet appointments are millionaires. And it's not that there is anything wrong with being a millionaire, as long as the wealth was obtained honestly. It's just that Mr. Clinton is presenting us with the same old hypocrisy behind the public facade of 'caring more' that's so galling.

Here is a joke I adapted: What's the difference between God and the Democrats? God knows everything. But the Democrats know everything better. Go ahead and laugh until you cry. The joke is on us for not already solving the problem by changing the Federal Republic to a National Democracy.

The same device of massing power and concentrating it into a tiny number of people 'to protect the citizens from themselves' has been used by every totalitarian government in the present and the last two centuries, including the oppressive government that ours has mutated into over the last thirty years. As long as you feel powerless and despaired about the government, the five hundred and forty-five know you won't take any steps to do anything about it. They don't care. They don't have to.

The five hundred and forty-five know that any real solution requires the elimination of their sovereign power to rule over the two hundred sixty millions of the rest of us. They know they can only remain in charge by pitting Americans against one another, thereby weakening our collective power. Their shadow show for the public's consumption continues while behind the curtain they invent new ways to confuse, rob and loot the citizens of our Nation of freedom and wealth. They have already stolen our Christian culture which is our only true inheritance.

Americans shouldn't judge all Christians or Christianity by the divisive and confused misanthropes who use the guise of religion to generate millions of dollars. Never forget that those who make a living in the news media attacking individual Christians are by their own example and admission decisively anti-Christian. And don't condemn yourself for the words and deeds of sociopathic liars like Lyndon Johnson, Richard Nixon or Bill Clinton.

Americans, as I envision you, the two hundred sixty millions not in federal office are together the inheritors of all that the Christian Founders imagined for our Nation, not those currently in power. Your wisdom and your willingness to think and hope in spite of all the deliberate confusion put forth by the majority of the five hundred and forty-five and their anti-democracy legions is the only force that has a chance to resolve the problems we face. Your act of demanding that there be only one issue, that of immediately amending the Constitution to peacefully change the government from a Federal Republic to a National Democracy as outlined herein, and then likewise each state government and municipality and school district, will unify the country in a way that no other action ever has.

All the problems that can be solved, will be solved with fairness and equity once you the citizens are sovereign. The five hundred and forty-five lawmakers will still be here to advise you, but on the citizens' terms. The corrupt seniority system in the House and Senate will disappear with the Federal Republic. At last, we will finally be free to choose leaders that we really want.

In 1776 there were American-born colonists in opposition to American independence. Thousands believed the British had the sovereign right to rule over the colonies and all its peoples, to consider them as property. Many fought shoulder-to-shoulder with the British. Still more left the country for England or Canada. Thomas Foley's ongoing example of leading the anti-Democracy forces to overturn the term limits legislation passed last year in my home State demonstrates more completely than any other example I can give you that you must expect the same obstruction from the majority of the five hundred and forty-five currently in office.

James Madison wrote eloquently in the Federalist papers about tyranny when power is concentrated into the hands of a few individuals. Thomas Jefferson, especially, labored to find the perfect balance between ideals and means for the brand new Nation as it existed over two centuries ago. But whatever nightmare their dream has mutated into, you must never forget that the Founders wanted Democracy. They only settled for a Republic because they hadn't the technical means to implement one. They couldn't gather all the voters together to vote on each piece of legislation. With television, telephones and computers we do have the means. All we lack is the will.

A republic can only attempt to represent the citizens fairly wherein men and women of honor, truth, knowledge, thrift, wisdom, clear-thinking ability and integrity serve as office holders. The representatives of a republic must be just that: They must be representative of the average person who lives in the Nation. In other words, they must be guided by Christian principles. The majority of the five hundred and forty-five have none of above-described characteristics in spite of whatever lies they utter to the contrary. And what's even more tragic is they don't even recognize it because of their situational ethics.

By his own admission, the English actor Peter O'Toole was an alcoholic for decades. When pressed by his friends to do something about his drinking problem he had declared proudly, 'What problem?'

Those in National office have the same problem except they are intoxicated by power. But even with the damage they have done it doesn't have to matter any more if you the citizens act now to amend the Constitution and become sovereign over the government.

Expect every opportunist to line up with House Speaker Thomas Foley and Bill Clinton and the rest of the anti-Democracy forces. Among them will be government employees, the news media and of course, the lobbyists and special interest groups--especially homosexuals and lesbians. You will easily recognize them because they will be the ones calling names like 'racist', 'sexist', 'extremists', 'bigot', 'homophobes', 'religious right', etc. The office holders in federal and state governments will make an extreme fuss and may very well hang on to the death just like their communist counterparts of the ex-Soviet Union.

After squandering a lifetime to acquire their positions and power under the Federal Republic, they are by and large unsuited for any practical work out here with the rest of us and they know it. They are used to collectively wielding absolute power. National Democracy will bring a practical end to their lives as they have always known it and very likely imprisonment for at least some of them. They won't give up easily but in the end, they will have no choice. There are only five hundred forty-five of them and two hundred sixty million of us.

You can expect to hear any lies and false charges against Americans who support National Democracy. You will also be a witness to their persecution. Those in power have a death grip on keeping the Nation divided. Yet in the end, the five hundred and forty-five lawmakers are like nothing more than the Sirens beckoning Ulysses to destruction on the rocks with their hallucinogenic rhetoric. You must not listen. Bill Clinton's leadership is like the Phantom of the Opera beckoning us to follow him into the twisted confusion of the darkness of his mind. All he has to offer is his totalitarian agenda and your own demise. Don't let him seduce you any longer. Learn to just 'say no' to anything he offers, except his resignation!

Americans must unite under one common banner of National Democracy. All political issues other than changing the Federal Republic to a National Democracy are symptoms of the absence of the citizens' sovereignty over the three branches of government. All other issues are only a subterfuge to divide us. There must be one issue and one alone until the citizens are sovereign. Then you will decide everything item by item by vote of the majority.

CHRISTIANITY AND DEMOCRACY

The *Declaration of Independence* states that we as a people have the right to change the government at any time. This and other such rights are not given to us by Congress nor by the President nor by the Supreme Court. They come from God.

Only Christians perceive their relationship with their Creator in this way. That is precisely why the five hundred and forty-five lawmakers in Washington D.C. do not want you or your children to learn about Christianity.

Jesus Christ was the very first person who ever lived to teach a philosophy based upon forgiving your enemies and actually loving them and doing good things to them instead of subjugating or killing them. Peaceful persuasion is one of the most important ideological building blocks of democracy. Without it and several of the other unique and essential messages of Christ, democracy cannot exist.

It is obvious that the fact our rights come from God and not government is exactly why Christianity has been expunged from our public institutions. This was done, especially over the past thirty years, under the guise of the separation of church and state. Those in power want us to 'feed from their fist' like pet birds. It has nothing to do with prohibitions against State religion.

If you look at any public opinion poll from any time over the last twenty years you find themes that are consistent throughout. For instance, the majority of citizens consistently want certain acts passed by the government. Among these are a balanced budget, voluntary prayer in public schools, etc. It's a long list. Why is it that the majority never gets what it wants? The reasons are complicated and you already know them. But the good news is that you already know the solution because the way out is very simple. It can be summed up in one word: Democracy.

Like it or not, the history of Western Civilization is the history of Christianity. All of the so-called ethical systems of Western Civilization are in fact renamed moral laws of the Bible and the New Testament. Jesus Christ's teachings, which were rooted upon Judaic law, serve as the basis of all our laws.

Does this come as a surprise? If you have never studied the Bible in depth and its effect upon Western Civilization over the last two thousand years you can hardly be considered educated. I say this not to chastise but to enlighten.

But my point here is whether or not you believe in God, or have studied the Bible or not, whether you agree or disagree with any or all of the teachings contained therein, you need to realize that the Government is not granting us the rights spelled out in the Declaration of Independence and the U.S. Constitution. They were recorded in those documents. But even if the Constitution had never been written, even if there had never been a United States of America, you would still possess these rights. Among them is the right of self government which includes the right to change the form of government with the agreement of the majority your fellow citizens. The Founding Fathers understood this extremely well. You began life possessing such rights.

If you can for even a moment disregard what some have done in the past in the name of Jesus Christ and read for yourself what Jesus said, you will discover that He was the originator of the concepts of true freedom, complete equality and total brotherhood. He alone founded the first society based upon total love and absolute respect for other humans as well as for the Creator.

But be prepared. As the Democracy movement grows, the picture of terror and loss of individual freedom the majority of the five hundred and forty-five and the rest of the anti-democracy forces will paint to confuse and frighten you will be absolute.

To the majority of the five hundred and forty-five lawmakers in power and the news media who serve them, Christians are portrayed as, at best, confused and at worst as Fascists. But because of what we actually believe in, and not in spite of our faith, once Democracy comes about, true individual freedom in the society will be multiplied manyfold. Not diminished.

ELECTIONS AND VOTING

Thousands in America have said recently that public office should not necessarily be a job for life. Under National Democracy it would be up to the majority of citizens alone if Supreme Court members should have term limits. The same would be true for every Federal office or any commissioner including the Presidency. I believe that not only should they have term limits but should be subject to recall as well at every election (no confidence vote). I recommend general elections at least every ninety days until Americans get used to ruling themselves.

To remove a president from office under the current Federal Republic the Senate has to bring a criminal indictment, hold a trial and secure a conviction. The process is called impeachment. Under National Democracy a simple 'no confidence' vote by the majority of citizens in any general election would oust the office holder the next day.

Bill Clinton has been President long enough for the public to get to know him well. According to the public opinion polls, the majority is disenchanted enough by what they have learned that, if it were within the voter's power, Mr. Clinton and his entire administration would certainly be recalled from office. Right now you the citizens lack the legal mechanism.

The vast majority of American's know you've made an absolute blunder in allowing Bill Clinton to be elected. Even his greatest fans in New York and Hollywood are making unmerciful jokes about him. When Democracy is created and you have the right of recall no ignoble incompetents will be left to linger in any office.

NEWS MEDIA

*'Stay tuned for more news
after these very important messages.'*

Television and radio channels are granted theoretically in public trust. Does the Public really own the air waves? It's a good question. Do the current Federal lawmakers have the right to rescind broadcasting rights? They claim they do. Would it be censorship? Under the existing Federal Republic it certainly would be censorship. The so-called Fairness Doctrine as currently proposed by the Congress adds more weight to this conclusion. (Read the chapter on the same topic.)

Books, films and movie theaters are all private and are therefore protected under the First Amendment. No matter what arguments are brought against Democracy, the majority of citizens will have the right to collectively to govern the Public airways once Democracy is realized. It will be interesting to witness what happens once Congress is forced to give up their self-serving monopoly over public broadcasting.

Daytime television, especially the talk show format, seems to serve the same function as the circus freak shows did one hundred years ago. Personally, from what very little I've been able to stomach, I think that these types of shows must appeal to those who are addicted to wallowing in irrational bouts of confused self-loathing and gender identity disorders.

I've also heard complaints about daytime soap operas but I've never seen one for more than a few moments. It just looks like talking heads to me. Boring. I generally agree with the author who wrote in the early 1970's that American television is the 'Great American Wasteland.' After all, television is entirely make believe. Every thing is staged and edited--even the so-called 'Live Cops' shows. T.V. sports are also nothing more than show business. Even the best T.V. programs are nothing more than one long 'commercial' to mentally condition you to buy commodities and spend your money to purchase a certain 'lifestyle' that the advertisers will sell to you.

Radio is similar to television with regard to advertising. There are dozens of stations on A.M. and F.M. to choose from. But as long as one is not compelled to listen, the public demand should determine what's available. Try removing all televisions from your house for a year as I once did. You'll discover just how boring T.V. really is compared to what else you could be doing. You won't miss anything.

The boycotts against advertisers who sponsor offensive television is interesting but misdirected because this whole issue is a symptom of a greater problem. Those people should concentrate on changing the government to a Democracy to get what they want.

The news of the world is an entirely different matter. It should be objective but it's not. It's evident that the presentation of the nightly news is deliberately managed to be bad, frightening and unbalanced.

Each network has a slightly different political bent to the left of the political mainstream. What they all have in common is that the you the viewer are shown terrible problems for five minutes. Then on comes the commercial with the solutions for two minutes.

What's the antidote to the bad economic news and plant closures as whole industries are transferred to Mexico? A vacation in Hawaii! Gang rape by professional football players? Hemorrhoid cream! Drive by murders of teen age honor students plus slaughter of innocent children by government agents in Waco, Texas? Extra strength pain relief! Starving children and economic oppression and riots in Los Angeles? Electronic home security! Everyone knows that luxury cars will instantly transfer you from the freeway to empty European mountain roads where your can screen out all the poor people, crying voices, pollution and all the other problems in the world--problems, as you've been told by the majority of the five hundred and forty-five lawmakers, that you personally allowed to happen since yesterday's news. But, since you're obviously guilty, drink a case of beer. You'll be instantly surrounded by young and voluptuous women with little clothing and easy sexual access. Soon you won't know anything and you won't care. If you're a loan shark and you've just had a rough week of breaking thumbs, check into a luxury hotel and get a free massage.

Bah! Whether they realize it or not the reporters are in fact nothing more than pain relief peddlers. And not very glorified ones.

If they don't know it yet, the people who buy the advertising time do. And now you do too. Don't allow yourself fall into their black hole of manufactured gloom.

The majority of the five hundred and forty-five lawmakers give tacit approval to the current form the news takes because they are intimidated by the pain relief peddlers (The PACS.) Also, the hopeless messages put forth nightly gives the elected officials encouragement and, in their own minds, a mandate to take over all aspects of modern life.

Here is an example of another problem: Two years ago, I watched television as yet another major bridge in my home State of Washington broke up and sank in deep waters during a winter storm. It happens every decade or so. Washington State is famous for it. (We don't just have erupting volcanoes and rain to entertain us.) On the nightly national news they showed various eyewitness and video tape accounts of the bridge breaking up and sinking.

It was reported as a great tragedy and loss, which of course, it was. For thirty years I lived within five miles of the bridge and used it several times a week before it was closed for repair. The circumstances of how and why it sank on that particular day is worthy of an entire book dedicated to government stupidity.

But as I watched the national news over the next few days to compare it to the local news, two different stories evolved. Nationally, the reporters said that the federally funded Interstate 90 link with Seattle, connecting the city to all parts East, was lost for years. Nowhere in the national reports did I hear that the bridge that sank was not at that time being used but was in fact under repair. Nowhere in the national coverage did I hear that all of the Interstate 90 traffic that used to cross on the now-sunken bridge was in fact crossing a brand new bridge built right next to the old one that had sunk. I'm sure that for a few days at least, the drivers and owners of the interstate trucking companies and would-be travelers to Seattle bought a few more tubes of hemorrhoid cream to sooth the ache.

It's important to realize that those in the Media are only following the examples of speaking half truths given by the majority of five hundred and forty-five lawmakers in power in Washington D.C. When the highest office holders in the land can't tell truth from fiction, or are loath to do so, what are we to expect from the news media?

I hope that, under Democracy, we will require the networks to report the news in a balanced way without commercials. It should be the price for the free gift of control of the airwaves.

WELFARE

'Freedom Equals Responsibility.'

Leo Thorsness

Congressional Medal of Honor recipient
and former Washington State Senator

Starting in 1964, under President Lyndon Johnson's Administration, a proliferation of programs were passed to help disadvantaged people. It was obvious then, as it is today, that millions of poor people needed and deserved special assistance. Lyndon Johnson became President in November 1963 when President John Kennedy was assassinated in Dallas, Texas. Johnson was already perceived by political insiders in America as the most feared, ruthless and skillful liar of the period. Compounding his political problems was the widespread opinion that Johnson had Kennedy assassinated.

But as a practical political matter, John Kennedy was killed only twelve months before the next presidential election. President Johnson had only a very short time to either change the voters perception of him or to find a new base of supporters.

It was also reported that Kennedy had picked Johnson to be his running mate in 1960 because as President, Kennedy didn't want to have to capitulate to the Texan (as Senate Leader) on every item he wanted passed in the Congress.

Johnson's life and voting record up until that time had represented the antithesis of what was then called liberalism. As the Senate Majority leader, Johnson had personally guided the 'States Rights' segregationist legislation of the 1950's and successfully killed most Civil Rights legislation before it could even get out of committee. Nevertheless Johnson then decided that the uneducated poor, who knew the least about him, would be the most likely to vote for him in the 1964 Election if he could do something to get them politicized. So, to secure victory in 1964 he became the Champion of the Nation's poor and of the racial minorities. He directed the passage of the landmark Civil Rights legislation. The so-called 'Great Society' was born. The poor and minorities were the means to his ascent.

To counter Mr. Johnson's utterly astonishing 180 degree political turn, (Actually a leap!) the Republicans squashed the political moderates within their party (Nelson Rockefeller) and put forth the arch-conservative, Barry Goldwater. Goldwater/Miller. AU H2O. 'In you're heart you know he's right.' Changed by some wag to, 'In your guts you know he's nuts.'

For one year out of his long and infamous political career, Lyndon Johnson did the right thing for the wrong reasons. After the election was won, Johnson abandoned the outward pretence of helping the poor and racial minorities. He returned to his former practice of enriching himself and his long-time supporters by looting the taxpayers. Lyndon Johnson committed U.S. troops to the war in South Vietnam, which he blamed on John Kennedy. Johnson sent these same poor and minorities off to fight and be killed in Vietnam, but never in numbers sufficient to finish off the enemy. Fortunately by then the long overdue Civil Rights legislation passed and the momentum carried on without Johnson's direct attention. From Mr. Johnson's perspective, Civil Rights legislation served only to take American's attention off his real agenda; enriching himself.

Beginning in 1964, young, economically disadvantaged women were told that if they were single and pregnant or had several or more children but no husband they could collect welfare payments, receive subsidized housing and food stamps and health insurance and a host of other benefits indefinitely. But, if they found or created a job or got married it would all end.

What happened? We all know that among the poor especially, this practice destroyed the basic family unit. In New York City and in several major cities the rate of poor women having children without a legal spouse is as high as 70%. Although this book is about conclusions and not facts, let me state that every study I've seen points to the same basic truth: In spite of heroic efforts on the part of women to raise children as single parents, the odds of a young person growing up and getting involved with crime, gangs, prostitution, drugs, dropping out of school, getting murdered, sentenced to prison and an a host of other problems is tied directly to one condition: No father in the home. If the child has a father in the home in addition to a mother, the odds of falling permanently into the traps listed above are tiny. My point is that poverty itself does not cause crime, contrary to what we are being told by the majority of the five hundred and forty-five lawmakers.

Even the poorest person in the United States is rich compared to most of the world's inhabitants. As a measure, in 1990 the average Gross Domestic Product per person in the U.S.A. was just under $19,000. I was raised poor by American standards but as an adult I've taken the opportunity to travel to other countries to see what it's like for myself. People in the United States who have never left the country have no idea what poverty is like in other countries. In Canada and England and France I saw conditions very similar to the U.S.A. But in central Mexico, where the average Gross Domestic Product in 1990 was $1,900 per person, I saw large numbers of people living in conditions that makes the worst neighborhoods I've seen in South Chicago, New York City, Florida or rural Mississippi look luxurious by comparison. In places like India and Ethiopia the GDP is only a few hundred dollars per year. Those people are POOR. But most do not become criminals because the children are raised by a mother and a father.

If arbitrary economic and social discrimination in itself caused crime, our courts and prisons would be over flowing with women, not men. The root cause of crime lies elsewhere. I offer several conclusions in the chapter on Safe Streets.

I was raised at the poorest end of an industrial working class community. It's worth sharing here that I'm speaking from my own experiences and personal conclusions.

My parents became adults during the great depression of the 1930's. My mother was an orphan and my father was forced to drop out of high school to support his family. Both my parents became factory workers. That period of economic upheaval was certainly greater than anything this current generation has ever known. Few if any Americans are suffering in the country today compared to then.

The crime rate of the 1930's did not increase significantly compared to today because of poverty. Why? Because the families stayed together. Christian values were taught and embraced by the majority of the citizens including the public schools.

They knew that common sense, which is based upon God's laws as taught in the Bible, wasn't to be cast aside just because of poor circumstances or bad feelings.

When I was a child, my father used to shovel coal in a steel mill for minimum wages or would work any other job he could get as a machine operator. He also made coiled springs, which requires a great deal of skill and knowledge and physical labor. It was considered unskilled because the trade was not unionized. As a consequence the wages were not much above the minimum.

He also worked on the side as a self-employed person making coiled springs whenever he could find or create work. There were many times when he had no work but he tried every day. My mother worked full time in a bakery or in a factory until she retired at age sixty-five.

My father didn't drink and as far as I remember he always came home at the end of his long work day. And although he often worked two jobs, eighteen hour days, six or seven days at a time, he still managed to go to daily Mass at our Church. Amazingly, he was also a well-read person.

He was sick primarily from industrial pollution all his adult life. He finally died from a combination of industrial diseases at age sixty-four. His last year of life was spent battling with cancer but not one of his dozen brothers and sisters ever came to our home even once just to visit or offer him any comfort yet he never said a word against them. He was not a success from the world's view and certainly not in his sibling's eyes but in memory of all that he did for me I have dedicated this book to him.

Why am I telling you this deeply personal information? It's because my father loved me. He wanted me to grow up and have a better life than he had known. He showed me by his example how to try and not to quit. He wanted me to know and be blessed and loved by God. I wanted my father to love me, just as my brothers and sister did. It was not easy. He wasn't perfect, and he didn't have a lot of information that people who are middle class or wealthy have. But the point is that he was there. We all wanted him to be proud of us. As best as we were able, all of us became what he and my mother wanted us to be.

My parents lived together as husband and wife until my father died. They had each other and little else by the way of material possessions and no outside family support. They were held together by adversity as much as their love for each other. My brothers and sister and I were an expression of that love. My father's Christian faith sustained him through impossible ordeals. What we all had in common was that we had the same mother and father. It was instinctive that we wanted his approval and could obtain it by trying to please him.

As far as Welfare is concerned, the problem is that over the past thirty years tens upon tens of millions of Americans have already grown up with no father in the home. Their teachers in school have been forbidden to teach Christian principles. Young boys grow into men and are by nature going to follow the most dominate male influence in their lives.

Based upon the fact that the government destroyed the basic family unit of the poor by removing the father, that the young men would be preyed upon by criminals and organized into violent gangs and every horror that goes with it is as predictable as night following the day for anyone with even a small measure of common sense.

It was the majority of the five hundred and forty-five lawmakers that said children of poor mothers cannot have a father in residence. They are wrong. It is self-evident that men and women belong together as husbands and wives to raise children. Any other arrangement is unnatural and unhealthy.

Once Democracy is realized, to begin to undo the damage done over the last thirty years, in addition to all the other changes, the citizens should vote that a condition of Welfare should be that a women must be married to collect the full payment.

I can hear the howls of protest now from all corners. But consider this, the citizens will be sovereign. The great wisdom of the majority will prevail at last. There have always been people in temporary or ongoing need through no fault of their own. I myself am an example of this. If the majority carry out my other or similar recommendations (especially regarding wealth creation), there will soon be full employment in perpetuity for all Americans.

The first people who will be the happiest about the changes regarding Welfare will be the young children. Every child wants a father whose love and attention are available daily. It is a basic human need. The common sense word is 'instinct'.

Next, the women and men recipients of welfare will be happy as the families of the poor and the victims of crime can begin healing after a third of a century. It will take some time to recreate natural and rational husband and wife family life among the poor but it will happen. Finally, the rest of the citizens, those who out of concern pay for Welfare and the overhead of the Criminal Justice system will begin to be happy as the costs decrease. There is no knotty problem that exists today that the citizens won't unravel in time.

As I quoted at the beginning of this chapter, 'Freedom equals responsibility.' This thought occurred to Leo Thorsness during his six year confinement in the 'Hanoi Hilton' during the Vietnam war. To achieve true freedom, each one of us is going to have to assume responsibility for ourselves and our Nation. Freedom is what changing from Republic to Democracy is all about. Democracy will bring true freedom. It will bring changes and people everywhere will have to grow as individuals and as groups to adapt to the new opportunities, responsibilities and expectations of Democracy.

The knowledge of men and women bonded in matrimony and as parents has been common sense for millennia in every culture on every continent in every age for all but the tiniest percentage. Only here and only because of the conditions laid down for collecting welfare has it changed.

RACISM

'I may not get there with you. But we as a people

will get to the Promised Land.'

Dr. Martin Luther King, Jr.

Dr. Martin Luther King, Jr. was a great American. His words and example have often inspired me to do things I might have otherwise been too timid to try, including writing this book. The biography, *'Let the Trumpet Sound'* by Stephen B. Oates is a fine tribute to him and to those who were inspired to act responsibly and change the minds of the lawmakers who ruled the nation. Every American should read it.

I've often wondered how many Americans who aren't Christian or Jewish, know that Dr. King, an ordained Christian minister, was paraphrasing Moses in the now immortal phrase quoted above?

For all of his adult life right up until his assassination, Dr. King struggled to bring the principles of Jesus Christ--true and perfect freedom, the basis of Democracy--to life for African Americans. By his leadership example he brought more freedom to all other racial minorities.

The schools close for Dr. King's birthday, but it is a tragic irony that public school teachers are forbidden to teach the very principles that inspired and guided him all his life. Dr. King insisted to the Nation that the teachings of Jesus Christ and the freedoms He promised, on which the United States of America were founded, be also given to People of Color.

The children of Israel emerged from the desert of Sinai after forty years of wandering (this after several centuries of slavery in Egypt). They moved in and possessed the 'land of milk and honey', the Promised Land, which God had given to Abraham their father.

Thanks to leaders like Martin Luther King, Jr. African Americans have done the same thing in their own home.

Thanks to Dr. King and millions of Americans who had enough of the division imposed upon us by the five hundred and forty-five lawmakers, over the last forty years, racism has diminished in America to the point that if you enter a public building, business, factory, restaurant, ballpark or University or anywhere else and in television and in films, you can see by examining the faces that no racial group is excluded. That's quite a change from when I was a child.

The shameful laws of slavery and later those of segregation that the five hundred and forty-five lawmakers of our nation's past created and enforced to exploit and divide Americans from one another no longer exist. Today many of the highest income earners in our nation are African Americans. Professional actors, comics, singers and athletes especially have proved that individual racial minorities today can achieve excellence and be rewarded for it by Americans of all races. I use entertainment for my example because there are no racial quotas to confuse the issue in this industry.

Based upon the dollars earned, Michael Jackson is the greatest entertainer in all history. What ever may come of the current allegations of sexual abuse against him, in his relatively young and brilliant life Mr. Jackson has worked for every penny of his billion dollar fortune. Quarterback Warren Moon has earned every penny of his multi-million dollar annual contact by being a better football player than all the rest of the players on his team. Ken Griffey, Jr. delights the nation, especially those baseball fans here in Seattle, with his ability to entertain with the wooden bat and leather glove. Bill Cosby is the highest paid person on television because he is a funny man and one of the best actors alive. What Whoopi Goldberg, Oprah Winfrey and Natalie Cole, just to name a few, have in common with those named above is that they have earned success by creatively and legally giving their audience exactly what they want. It's a simple and very old formula. The good news is, anyone can use it of any race or any economic background.

Old feelings of hurt from racism may still exist in the hearts of some Americans. Perhaps most of them. African Americans may feel bitterness, anger, humiliation, fear or despair-but those are only feelings. There are no laws upholding racism any more. Racism as the dominant, legal, and political barrier to success is no longer a fact in the United States. Racism is now legally as much a part of the past as is slavery. The majority of poor people in the United States are Caucasians and not African Americans or Hispanics. And I've learned through decades of peer-counseling that it always comes as a surprise to non-whites to learn that poor and working class, middle class and even wealthy Caucasians are often full of the bitterness, anger, fear, humiliation, powerlessness, confusion and great despair just as are Blacks, Hispanics and Native Americans.

At workshops for teachers of peer-counseling, I've counseled people from every continent, every race, every social and economic class. These feelings are part of all forms of economic oppression which comes from relative scarcity. These feelings are part of the universal human condition and all humans experience them beginning very early in life (whether you want to believe it or not). Many Christians believe that this situation will remain until Jesus Christ returns. I believe the condition will be around at least as long as relative scarcity exists. (Refer to chapter on Space Exploration.) Whatever your own evaluation, the only way out of the problems still remaining begins with ending blame and embracing this and the other principles Jesus taught and then taking rational action.

My point is, whatever your background, and in spite of your feelings, you don't have to act as if the past still exists because it doesn't. It's a message for all Americans. As a people we must all put aside our old feelings and act on what we think we should be done today. Today we can listen to the voices of reason and take real steps to end whatever vestiges of oppression that still exist by changing the government to Democracy.

Gang leaders, rap singers, Aryan Nations and politicians who preach racial hatred are themselves trying to recreate a past that no longer exists. They are afraid that only way they can earn money, stay in the spotlight and have personal power is by trying to re-ignite the spent and cold embers of racism. Blacks especially should not let themselves be divided from other Americans. Instead, they should seek true freedom and justice through Democracy.

In 1992, David Duke tried to re-ignite racism for Caucasians. To use another analogy, Mr. Duke played the old broken record of racial prejudice for an audience that no longer accepts the message. His lack of results did also serve to show how completely racial prejudice has died in the hearts of the vast majority of Americans. Just compare David Duke to George Wallace who played the same broken record in 1968 and succeeded in taking five states in the general election.

I know this contradicts the divisive message the majority of the five hundred and forty-five lawmakers as well as that of some African American leaders who are still trying to divide us. They are still using the issue of racism to divide us in order to take our attention off of their real agenda.

You might be asking yourself, 'If racism no longer exists, why do I still feel so miserable and why is my life so hard? People still treat me terribly!' The answer is that you need to have Jesus Christ as your savior and Lord. You need to be filled with the Holy Spirit of God. That is what's still missing! You have a big hole inside of you that can only be filled by the living Spirit of God. God will fill you with love and joy beyond measure and heal your pain and give you the wisdom and knowledge and the cooperation of others to solve any and all of your remaining problems. If you don't believe me study the New Testament and ask God to reveal directly to you whether it's true or not.

After Democracy is realized, the voices in Washington D.C. will no longer be paid to divide Americans. When they are no longer confusing us it will be much easier for individuals in the society to work toward personal prosperity and freedom. After the federal budget is changed by you as I've outlined in the chapter of the same title, everyone who wants a good productive job will have one. It will then become crystal clear that what is actually missing today is the wisdom, love and peace of mind which can only come from God. The two hundred sixty million of us who are about to be empowered through Democracy need to forgive one another for whatever happened in the past and especially for what failed to happen in the past due to the poor leadership of the five hundred and forty-five federal republican lawmakers.

GAY RIGHTS

The lawyers in the Temple repeatedly asked Jesus to comment (about a women caught in sexual sin) and eventually he told them, 'If any of you is without sin, let him be the first to throw a stone at her.' At this, those who heard his words began to go away one at a time, the oldest ones first until only Jesus was left, with the women still standing there. Jesus asked her, 'Woman, where are they? Has no one condemned you?' "No one,' she answered. Jesus said, 'Then neither do I condemn you. Now go and leave your life of sin.'

John: Chapter 8

The first truly national political victory for Gay Rights occurred in the early 1980's. As soon as the AIDS disease was discovered, the homosexuals were able to exercise their political power over the five hundred and forty-five lawmakers to prevent widespread testing. This was power that the general Public did not know homosexuals had.

AIDS is a deadly communicable disease. But unlike all deadly outbreaks in the past, homosexuals were able to change the issue from one of Public Health to one of Civil Rights. No widespread testing was allowed so homosexuals continued to infect each other. Today AIDS is the number one cause of death among males between the ages of 25 to 44 in U.S. cities of 100,000 population or more.

Under the Federal Republic, homosexuals have great power relative to their numbers, though at most only a tiny percent of the total population is practicing that form of behavior exclusively. To accomplish what they want as a group, just as any foreign lobbyist knows, homosexuals know they don't have to bother changing the minds of the majority of American citizens. With tens of millions of dollars to buy influence plus fanatical political activism, gays have learned they only have to convince the majority of the five hundred and forty-five lawmakers who comprise the three branches of the Federal Government to get exactly what they want. They do the same thing at the State and Local levels using the same methods.

The next major victory for Gay Rights came in the late 1980's in the form of Federal taxes to find a cure for AIDS. This year there is as much public tax revenues going to AIDS research compared to cancer research even though there are ten times as many cancer patients.

In 1992, homosexuals gave Bill Clinton the financial edge he needed to win the election. I've read that the financial figure was around three million dollars in donations. That may be as much as twenty three percent of what Mr. Clinton's campaign spent directly. Based upon Mr. Clinton's agenda for the first year in office, it is crystal clear that the homosexuals were the one and only group he felt he had to pay off no matter what the social and financial cost to the rest of the U.S. citizens.

I realize that the homosexuals in general are not happy with the President's 'Don't ask, don't tell.' proclamation for the military. Mr. Clinton offered his own lifelong personal political axiom *Don't ask me any questions and I'll tell you no lies.* Publicly, some homosexuals have decried the 'compromise' yet, all things considered, and in spite of Mr. Clinton's cynical duplicity, it is a total victory for them considering the prior policy. In 1993 and because of Mr. Clinton's actions, the average citizen finally woke up to what Gay Rights actually means for America and just how well organized and well-financed the movement is.

Universal Health Care is the now the next and most important goal of the Gay Rights movement since most Americans with AIDS are homosexuals who have either lost or are in danger of losing their insurance coverage or cannot acquire coverage any other way. With Universal Health Care, (meaning the citizens' taxes paying for all treatments and medicines) homosexuals hope they can continue to practice their suicidal behavior with impunity knowing that public taxes will supply them with the expensive life-sustaining drugs their bodies require.

Gay leaders would like to establish that feelings alone are the basis for inclusion in their group. That's why their total estimates for the gay population are so wildly exaggerated. If you've been molested as a child, raped, propositioned or even had thoughts about same-sex, they include you in their calculations. But it remains a fact that homosexuality is defined by behavior. Homosexuals are what they are because as a way of life they engage in same sex practices. The so-called genetic link to homosexuality is a farce that can't survive even slight scientific inquiry.

Before AIDS was diagnosed in 1982, homosexuals had, more than any other identifiable group, more cases of syphilis, gonorrhea, hepatitis, herpes, recreational drug use, alcoholism, suicides, injuries due to foreign objects being inserted into their rectums, shortest life expectancy from other causes and some other specific life-threatening conditions. AIDS is merely the latest plague to strike those who habitually practice sexual sin. It won't be the last. Sin against God's laws carries it's own punishment and it always brings the same result: Death. All the hysteria about 'homophobes' aside, this is very useful information.

No Christian is condemning homosexuals. Our position is the same as Jesus, 'Leave your life of sin.' (God loves the person, not the sin.) We know homosexuals are not their addiction, even if they don't. Because of this, under Democracy, and as an act of love, the majority should not allow homosexuality to be taught anywhere as normal and desirable as the homosexuals have now established in many places in America any more than we should tolerate the promotion of any other deadly addiction or suicidal behavior.

Within the Christian counseling community, the homosexuals who have been delivered from their addiction have reported that shame, fear and guilt has not been placed upon them by heterosexuals but by the homosexuals who raped, molested or seduced them in the first place. Through Jesus Christ, anyone can be 'born again' and receive a Divine new nature including healthy desires!

'Gay Rights' advocates should realize that it may be hundreds or even thousands of years before our nation becomes so far out of balance again where contradictory issues such as theirs are again made preeminent over the needs of husbands and wives, families, children, industrial workers, education and the poor. What has happened in the last thirty years has only been possible because of the breakdown in leadership brought about by the contradiction of five hundred and forty-five lawmakers trying to do the thinking for two hundred sixty million other Americans.

Gay Rights

Under Democracy, homosexuals will have the right to convince the two hundred sixty million of the rest of us of the reasonableness of their requests for tax monies and special privilege. Homosexuals are doubtless already preparing for this outcome. You can expect them to be among the most fanatically opposed to Democracy.

Women's Movement vs. Feminism

'Chiang Jhing -- Live Like Her!'

Chinese Woman's Movement slogan.

I believe that working class and poor women plus their children, remain the most politically and economically oppressed identifiable group in our Nation. Unquestionably, they have the most to gain from changing the Federal Republic to a National Democracy. Adult females are potentially the most powerful force in America because they outnumber men and could accomplish Democracy without the vote of one man. Unfortunately for these women, Feminists (who currently have the loudest voices) insist that only they alone understand what's best for American women.

Feminism in the United States of America in 1994 is a counterfeit, a mutation of the broad scale Women's Movement that surged across the Nation beginning in the late 1960's and throughout the decade of the 1970's. The Women's Movement itself traced it's Western roots back to the 1910's and 1920's. But the incredible surge in the recent two decades owed it's impetus to what was then taking place in China.

In Asia, a billion Chinese citizens were being politically, culturally and mentally prepared for a woman to become the Premier. That woman was Chiang Jhing, Mao Tse-Tung's wife and chief architect of the Chinese Cultural Revolution. Chiang Jhing, once an film actress, was exercising supreme power in her husband's name during his declining years through the private army she helped to create: the Red Guards.

She fully expected to succeed her husband when he died. For well over a decade she had de facto power of China's communist government, and its treasury and the forced cooperation of a billion people to lay the groundwork for her succession. 'Equal pay for equal work!', 'Women hold up half the sky!' and virtually all the slogans, issues and rhetoric of the U.S. Women's movement of the period were emanating from China.   Women's equality messages were erupting out of China like an exploding volcano. The accompanying social earthquakes were so powerful that they caused a tidal wave of change to roll across the oceans and wash ashore on the American continent half a world away flooding everyone and everything in its path.

In February of 1972, Richard Nixon became the first U.S. President to visit China. He was also the first prominent American with reporters in tow to be admitted since the Communists seized power in 1949. The communists in America had already known that China was the source of the great change toward women's issues. The reports broadcast of Nixon's visit showed the world what was happening.

Even though the Women's equality images and messages were flowing from another culture, a different language and a totalitarian State, because of what was wrong in America, they were received by and made much sense to U.S. women. This was especially true among young women of university age. They were the very first generation to have passed completely through primary and secondary public education in the post-Christian era.   These young adults were desperate for an ideology to fill the spiritual vacuum.

There are many books about the Women's movement of the 1970's. Some are extremely serious ideological works and others are simply stories about how individual women's lives were changed. In the face of the collapsing society, the Women's Movement appealed to and had a place for women of all ethnic, economic and educational backgrounds.   It changed in many aspects the way most women perceived themselves as women. For many women and even some men, it was a time of, and was rightly named, 'Liberation'.

Concurrently, that period of American history (1960 - 1975) has been defined as the first phase of open and public abandonment of Christian principles by our national leaders. They   flagrantly betrayed the trust of the American people by discarding the last ideals of democracy and championed their own totalitarian agenda. It is a gross understatement to say that there was a great vacuum in the American Spirit. (I maintain this in spite of many good things that came out of the Civil Rights Acts of the period which included the ban against sexual discrimination.)

In addition, in the early 1970's the average citizen of the United States was reeling from a collapsing economy and declining overall standard of living and disintegration of society as a result of the expensive and completely fruitless war in Vietnam that Lyndon Johnson, Richard Nixon and the rest of the five hundred forty-four lawmakers had given the country. Across the nation, everyone but especially middle and working class women were confronted with the fact that, not only were they compelled to leave homes to enter the work force in large numbers, but even with two incomes they could not maintain the standard of living they had enjoyed in the past. Poor women had already been working, but they were being hammered as never before by the inflation. There was no such thing as cost of living increases then. (Inflation should be called instead 'the cost of politics'.)

Hundreds of thousands of young wives, girl friends, mothers, children, brothers, sisters and parents were also trying to cope with the fact that sixty thousand of their young men would never be returning home from the Vietnam war. That war had and was still being fought by the young men of America's poor and working class. Hundreds of thousands of other young G.I.s had come home wounded or in wheel chairs. It was a war that America's leaders had no will to win even after ten long and bitter years of fighting.

More than anything, the Women's Movement in the United States brought attention to the problems confronting all Americans but especially to women because of the disintegration of the fabric of our Nation on all fronts. It gave specific answers for what to do about personal problems created by the lack of wise leadership from the highest offices.

When Mao Tse-Tung died in 1976, Chiang Jhing moved to make her new power official. But she was out-maneuvered. Chiang was arrested, tried, convicted of treason and sent to prison along with her main supporters by Deng Xiao-Ping, an old enemy of her husband. They were branded 'The Gang of Four'.

In America, Chiang's messages had temporarily filled the spiritual vacuum created when our National leaders officially abandoned our Christian principles (as I describe in other chapters). When she was silenced, the fountain of information and leadership regarding sexual equality abruptly stopped flowing.

Fortunately, by 1976, the laws of the United States which permitted discrimination against women had been changed. Women in America had long since been aroused to action.

I suspect that most American women weren't even aware that China had been the source of the great impetus of leadership nor that it had been abruptly turned off. I'm certain that only those who knew and fully understood what had transpired were the so-called 'China Watchers'.

The Women's Movement was originally centered around reaching out to and empowering all women, exactly as it had happened in China. Especially targeted for support were young women with children and families, older women and the poor. In every local community, centers were established by women for women's benefit covering the widest spectrum of interests. Interpersonal skills to enable women to act and think outside the role they had always lived were emphasized. Again, this was all modeled directly from the examples in China.

Unfortunately the model also included the Chinese Communist Party's doctrine that decreed women should abort all their children except one. The slogan, 'Every child a wanted child,' came directly from the Chinese Cultural revolution. Under this ideology, children are welcome only when it is the most convenient (meaning, of course, for the State).

Every neighborhood in China still has at least one women who is paid by the communist government to visit each home to enforce the one child per couple rule. Couples who defy the rules and fail to abort their second or more children are denied job opportunities and lose their housing rights. They are ostracized by the 'politically correct' (yet another phrase of the Cultural Revolution).

(In the Chapter titled 'Moscow', I discuss a little of my own personal history and how I came to my conclusions which follow.)

By the time Mao Tse-Tung died, (and Chiang Jhing was silenced) the American Women's Movement was entering its second decade since it had forced the Federal laws permitting discrimination against women to be changed. This was also the time when lesbian activists targeted the Women's Movement for takeover. In many ways their strategy offered them their greatest potential opportunity.

By the late 1970's, lesbians were quietly or assertively well along with their plans to take over virtually all the Women's Movement's official organizations. They did this by working harder and exhibiting more aggression. They proved my assertion that anyone who exhibits leadership will be followed to the extent they exhibit that quality, no matter how irrational the message.

You can hear the transition in the music of the period. Before 1980 most of the music from the Women's Movement was about fairness, equality, strength and improving themselves and their families' lives (which included men's lives). After 1980 the music celebrated lesbian love affairs and hatred of men.

Without Chiang Jhing's more or less rational messages of sexual equality, the American Women's Movement literature was abruptly refocused. The lesbian leaders, now officially in charge, changed the official goals. They substituted what is now called 'Feminism' but which is in fact only the lesbians' own narrow agenda.

Married and working class and poor women, housewives, mothers and especially Christian women were hounded out of women's organizations leaving them feeling betrayed, angry, inadequate or bewildered. The numbers of women officially involved shrank until only a tiny but extremely vocal number remained. By the mid 1980's only the lesbians and an even smaller number of very cynical and wealthy professional opportunists whose incomes and political power depended upon keeping up the facade were left.

It's now been well over a decade since Feminists completely stole the political currency of the American Women's Movement by counterfeiting it's name. The July 2, 1993 copy of U.S.A. Today contains another national writer's view of the National Organization for Women as just another arm of the Gay Rights movement. I must admit that I was surprised to find the U.S.A. Today report since, until recently, anyone who dared to publicly point out who Feminists really are was vilified.

According to various national news media sources, every candidate for the presidency of the National Organization for Women is an avowed lesbian or a bisexual. (NOW elections July 1993.) According to what I've read in various newspapers, the competition seemed to revolve around who could voice the most bazaar and extreme positions. You need to read them for yourself.

I have been told personally by Gay Rights advocates that they want to force the U.S. Federal Government to recognize four legal genders: (1) heterosexual men, (2) heterosexual women, (3) homosexual men and (4) lesbian women. It's been over ten years since I was personally informed that in time all human males will be hunted down and exterminated now that human cloning and invitro fertilization are possible. For decades the lesbians' definition of rape has been any sex act between a man and a women. Lesbians exalt abortion because every pregnant woman is evidence of male/female sexual intercourse. My own point here is not that the lesbians' woodenheaded concepts need to be accepted as a dark inevitable future. The issue is the utterly confused mentality of those advocating their deadly agenda. Yet Feminists know they don't have to convince you or me or the majority of Americans of anything. They only have to convince the majority of the five hundred forty-five lawmakers in Washington D.C.

I realize that Feminists reject what I have to say if for no other reason that I am a man and that they believe all relationships between men and women are inherently oppressive. Yet, I agree at least that for all non-Christian male & female relationships, this could very well be the case. It is true, as it says in the Bible, that men without the wisdom of God guiding them are no better than brute animals. In the early 1970's, women became quite eloquent in pointing this out. For example, the phrase, 'male chauvinist pig' could easily be a modern translation for many phrases describing godless men in the Bible. The only young women I know today are Christians and they never speak of this subject in my presence. And why should they after all? Their Christian husbands or Christian boyfriends are the only men in our Nation, besides Jewish men, that still act toward women with genuine equality and respect.

In 1975, I attended a Women's Conference at the Evergreen State College, in Olympia, Washington. I listened to a Black women speaker lamenting the loss of momentum of African American causes to the Women's movement. She warned the triumphant women that another cause could and probably would supplant or steal their momentum. She warned them to be on guard for it.

It seemed a surprising thought at the time. It didn't appear to me as if many of the women agreed with the speaker's sentiment or even understood what that new cause might be. Today, it's obvious what happened.

Politically, the so-called Feminists think it doesn't matter that they represent only the lesbian agenda (they deny it) because together with the male homosexuals they have succeeded in taking over or changing the policies and redirecting the goals of every organization they've targeted. These organizations include the

Department of Education, most civil rights organizations, many state and municipal governments, all the major news organizations (except CBN) and even the government of some denominational churches. (The U.S. military and health care are merely the latest targets.)

By dominating, bribing and intimidating the five hundred and forty-five lawmakers in Washington D.C., (plus their counterparts in every State and Local government) Feminists have acquired everything they originally set out to obtain. They know all too well that they don't have to convince or do anything for the masses of women in America.

The officials in power in Washington D.C. are witless and senseless enough from their lifetime of situational ethics to pretend publicly that these wealthy Feminists speak for all women. That's what the Feminists always proclaim for one another's benefit when the T.V. cameras are on. Privately the politicians are terrified of the lesbian's and homosexual's political power. With Bill Clinton and Hillary Rodham (their champions) and the Democrats in Congress to do their bidding, the lesbians and homosexuals now feel they are all powerful. So they think.

I predict that after Democracy, the force and the spirit of the Women's Movement as it existed in the mid 1970's, for and by the broad spectrum of all women, before the lesbians hijacked its momentum, counterfeited it's name and changed its agenda, will return. It will be reborn in wonderful ways that will eclipse anything those of us who were alive witnessed in that decade. I believe this because once the citizens are sovereign, women will comprise 51% of all the lawmakers. (There are more U.S. adult women alive than men.) Add to this the fact that most of the women in America still practice Christian principles and you have a formula for astonishing wonders.

The current generation of young women may not have a clue as to how things got the way they are now. I wonder sometimes if many of them care? With Madonna as their idol who can tell anything? In October 1993, PBS quoted a reporter who capsulated the formula for her 'great' success: *'She dresses like a whore and thinks like a pimp.'* Madonna is nothing more than another symptom that the young have been abandoned and that the vacuum of wise leadership is so great that anyone will be followed if they exhibit leadership, however irrational and self destructive their message.

Nevertheless, once women become the majority of lawmakers under National Democracy, the sheer wholesomeness of listening to the thoughts of and seeing the new laws designed and approved by the majority of American women will be a welcome relief.

Prepare yourself for Feminists to be among the most fanatically opposed to National Democracy side by side with the homosexuals and those currently elected to political office. Under Democracy, all groups seeking public support and funding will have to take their appeals directly to the majority of America's two hundred sixty million citizens. Together, American citizens are the most fair and generous people in the history of humanity. Without the special interests and the five hundred forty-five lawmakers to divide us, I'm confident all worthwhile causes will get the attention, support and public funding they deserve.

NATIONAL HEALTH INSURANCE

This subject and all its ramifications are worth volumes and many have already been written. In this short book I can only offer conclusions and a few critical observations. The coming National Democracy will assume all obligations of the existing Federal Republic regarding this issue. Once the citizens are sovereign, every American will have very good and affordable health care insurance. This will of course include prevention, health maintenance and proper nutrition.

The National Democracy will be able to afford this by creating more wealth and new opportunities than exist currently to pay for health care for every American. If you've read the rest of this book, especially the chapters on Income Tax and the Budget, you know the possibility for new wealth under National Democracy will eclipse anything the current five hundred and forty-five lawmakers in power ever dreamt of in their most wanton tax and spend delirium (their words for revenue and investment). The economic solution is not a new formula nor is it complicated.

It's worth noting that since the adoption of Medicare in the mid 1960's, that the average annual rate of increase for health care costs in the United States has been more than twice the rate of inflation. The medical doctors have had no incentive to reduce the costs to the Nation because those elected to Federal office were afraid to tell Seniors the true cost lest they lose the latter's votes. Between 1980 and 1990, for every dollar spent by the Federal government on children it spent twenty dollars on Seniors. This is an unprecedented situation in history. John Chancellor of NBC television news titled this situation, 'Honey, I robbed the kids!' The sad but simple explanation for this is that children don't have a PAC in Washington D.C.

The Seniors are told continuously by national retirement 'watchdog' organizations to vote against anyone who even questions this policy. What has it gotten them? Today over a third of the total annual national medical costs for all Americans are incurred to keep seniors alive for the last thirty days of life. From the government's own official estimate, this year alone medicare will spend

$180,000,000,000 dollars for last-second measures on seniors who are terminally ill. This is in addition to all the other money Medicare will spend for normal care as well as all other private insurance payments and doctor and hospital and nursing home bills paid from seniors' private estates.

I accept that when your life is ending you don't question the price to keep you and yours alive. But seniors want, need and deserve comforting at their death beds, not just another tube shoved up their nose. The Christian values of compassion and common sense need to be reintroduced into medicine. Medicare and Medicaid and all the other programs are being paid for out of money borrowed in the citizen's name by the Federal Government. This is money that they know they will never be able to repay. Seniors aren't the only citizens. How can someone ninety years old in a coma in the hospital whose only signs of life come from a machine make a rational decision? Under National Democracy, all Americans old enough to vote will have to decide together by voting item by item how much should be spent and how it should be spent.

The people who need health care the most and who have the least ability to pay for it are, by and large, young women with young children. They or their spouse, if they have one, might have jobs but few have health insurance. Under the current system of special interests, PACs and lobbyists, young mothers and their children are the least powerful politically. They have been passed over by the stronger Feminist lobby and their lesbian agenda. Yet they are the future of the Nation if there is going to be a Nation. Young mothers and their children must come first in any rational health care system. (Exactly the opposite of the current Federal Republic.) Instead of using the $180,000,000,000 (that's 180 billion) per year for desperate measures to keep comatose and terminally ill seniors alive for an extra thirty days, the National Democracy should use the money for those who have a future.

Today the homosexual community is pushing hardest for National Health Insurance. Bill Clinton promised it to gays along with his promise to lift the ban on homosexuals and lesbians in the military during the 1992 presidential campaign. They want national insurance so those of you in the productive sector, in the form of your taxes paid to the Federal Republic plus more borrowed trillions of dollars, can pay for the expensive drugs they need to stay alive. They could then continue to enjoy their suicidal same-sex practices with impunity from the deadly diseases which inevitably accompany such behavior.

The drugs, doctor visits and other treatments for AIDS can costs upwards of $100,000 per year or more per patient. And that's not counting the costs to treat all the other sexually transmitted diseases such as hepatitis, syphilis, gonorrhea, herpes and all other conditions such as alcoholism, drug addiction and aborted suicide attempts that homosexuals have in far higher percentages than any other single identifiable group. This information should have been part of the public debate over Bill Clinton's Federal health care proposal but it was concealed.

In August 1993, President Bill Clinton proposed his Federal health care plan to Congress. It's a very complex and emotional issue. Whatever plan is passed into law, it is a certainty that the average person will pay more and receive less benefits than they would under a private insurance plan. I predict that Mr. Clinton's plan will merely be another way for the five hundred and forty five Federal lawmakers to levy yet another payroll tax to pay more government employees to produce nothing without having to call it a tax. It is enough to say that his plan will fail utterly as all attempts at government price control programs have in the past and will have to be totally abandoned.

The health care program offered by the National Democracy should be administered by private insurance companies. It should be offered in insurance 'groups' to everyone. The National Democracy should do what it is able to do. In the short run the best way to reduce the costs of health care and increase the availability of services is through prevention. To that end the plan should include drug and alcohol counseling, and education and counseling to help Americans avoid following into the hallucinogenic notion that male with male anal intercourse is normal and natural (with or without a condom). Helping another person avoid a deadly addiction is one of the highest acts of love--not hate.

In the long run the best way to increase the availability of health care and decrease the cost is to increase the numbers of health care providers. The new government should encourage a four fold increase in the numbers of medical students and limit the damages that can be awarded in law suites for mental anguish against doctors and hospitals.

In November of 1993, Ms. Hillory Rodham Clinton launched a hysterical verbal attack against the health insurance companies of American for daring to have an opinion other than her own on the subject. Her focus was on the companies' 'crime' of earning profits. Someone should have pointed out to her forty years ago that without profits companies very quickly go out of business. The greatest 'crime' an insurance company can commit against its policy holders as well as against its employees is to fail to make a profit. Much could be written about her antics and her totalitarian agenda but it is enough to say that anyone who can think and reason is her enemy.

If there is a 'crime' being committed it is that a person who was elected by no one and therefore cannot be removed (Ms. Rodham Clinton) is wheeling such enormous power over us. Once Democracy is created by you the citizens the conditions which allowed Ms. Rodham Clinton to simply take power will end forever.

EMPLOYMENT

Taxes Up = Employment Down

Every time taxes are raised to pay people to produce nothing (the definition of government jobs) other jobs are lost in the productive sector (where all wealth is created). A recent Federal government study points out that the ratios are three to one. Three productive jobs lost for every patronage job created by the Government.

Over the years, I've read many private accounts that agree with the Government study but which break it out further. One job in the military costs five in the productive sector. One scientist to make weapons of mass destruction costs ten jobs in the private sector.

In the mid 1970's, I worked as an intern for the government under a joint Federal, State and Local crime control program sponsored by the Department of Justice. I worked on and off over a two year period at the Local and State levels.

I have one thing to say about it all, prefaced by a statement about my other work experiences: As a child I delivered papers with my brother. From my early teenage years until I graduated from college I worked either in my father's small factory making coiled springs or in other spring factories, or in road building shoveling hot asphalt under the summer sun and occasionally in the construction trades performing manual labor. After working for the government, I went straight into financial services and have been there up to the present. The point of my preface is that I know what it means to put in a productive day's work.

Based upon my admittedly limited experiences in government, I observed that everything you've ever heard or feared about the waste of money, time, manpower, political patronage, petty infighting, self-obsession and self-aggrandizement is understated by at least ten times. The places I worked, the only people that actually did anything were typists (mostly women) and copy and print shop machine operators. Career civil servants have not the first clue as to what work is like in the business world where owners, employees and managers are actually expected to accomplish something by creating a physical product or service that the public wants and can pay for. And if the business doesn't succeed they don't just lose their jobs but the business collapses and the investment is lost.

Take a simple example like coiled springs and wire forms which I know something about having made hundreds of thousands of them in my life. Even though you don't see them, springs and wire forms are in almost every manufactured device. Personal computers can have hundreds of them. Every key on the computer key board has a small spring inside to push the key back up after you strike it. Without a spring to return the key to the original position the electrical connection would never be broken. Once you typed the first key the computer would keep repeating it until you pulled the plug.

Using this simple example, my point is that wealth can only be created from physical substances and objects. Except for NASA, government employees don't create wealth directly or indirectly. And they don't have to care because in spite of their lofty-sounding rhetoric, official purposes and titles, their real job is to assist the majority of the five hundred and forty-five lawmakers to maintain sovereign power. I learned nothing but bad habits working for the government. According to their rhetoric, each act of the federal republicans currently in power has had as its origin a goal to enhance the welfare (the word originally meant wealth) of the public. Yet each act has turned into the opposite for the average American. The government denies this because from their perspective they have succeeded on all fronts with their real agenda. They know they are all powerful because they have finally succeeded in seizing control over the Nation politically, culturally and economically all at the same time. The contradiction is between the public good for which the acts were intended and the uses to which each has been put. The federal republicans must constantly conceal their real identity and agenda to remain sovereign. Those in power charge you a trillion dollars per year which they spend to keep you confused.

I also believe it is self-evident that the great majority of the politicians themselves stir up class hatred against the ambitious. I know from my industrial working class background that even the most unskilled lowest paid laborer understands that the worst crime a company can commit against its employees is to fail to make a profit. Without profits the company is in the first phase of economic collapse. Sadly, today anyone with the common sense to have a work ethic is a whipping post for the majority of the five hundred and forty-five lawmakers and the millions of their voters they pay not to produce anything. They punish everyone who adds directly to the wealth of the Nation with onerous taxes and for no other reason than to give themselves more power. It is self-evident that by taxing trillions of dollars from individuals and companies in the productive sector and borrowing trillions more to pay their reserve army of voters to produce nothing, and by pitting Americans against one another, they and they alone are responsible for creating the economic and social problems of our Nation.

Employees and owners of small to medium-sized business and investors cooperating together is the force that creates most of the wealth in this nation. It is a tragic commentary on our times and an indictment against the politicians that taxes alone cause many small family operated companies to go out of business.

The overall rise in average values for publicly traded stocks in 1993 and early 1994 appears on the surface to be good news for the Clinton administration. They are taking the credit. Yet, this rise was accompanied by declining earnings and massive layoffs, falling sales and a loss of market share for most domestic industries. This confounds 'conventional' investment wisdom that *'gains follow earnings'*. The so-called Clinton *Deficit Reduction* Plan (passed August 1993) not only raised the rates of tax on personal income but imposed an additional ten percent surtax on middle class and higher-income earners. So, in spite of the bad economic news, professional investors have shifted their wealth out of income and into equities. They are taking the risk that the economy will improve when Mr. Clinton leaves office in three years and that any gains in equities will not be taxed until they are sold. Equities can be pledged as collateral for tax free loans if the investor needs ready cash. They can enjoy any gains without paying taxes while they wait for the day when rates are again lowered. Then they can sell out and pay a reduced tax.

The problem for the economy, meaning the average American, is that this particular shift from income to equities means a shift from spending (consumption) to holding. Consumption drives the entire economy. Don't be fooled into a false sense of compliancy. Higher taxes combined with all the other follies of this administration will soon create a deep recession. As with all the other problems facing us, the only way you can put an end to all of this is to create a National Democracy.

SOCIAL SECURITY

'Father forgive them, for they know not what they do.'

Jesus Christ -- Luke 23:34

In 1976, Jimmy Carter was elected President claiming to be an outsider to national politics. He campaigned on several themes. Among them that the Social Security System was a 'disgrace' to the American people. Exactly what he meant by this was never made clear during his campaign. If you were a young person you could take it to mean that the Social Security tax would be eliminated. That was my own foolish impression at the time after listening to Mr. Carter. I was twenty-three years old. On the other hand, if you were a senior you could take him to mean that your benefits would be increased if you voted for Carter.

The result? After Carter was elected, Social Security taxes were increased and since that time they have gone up at an ever increasing rate. Seniors who voted in record numbers for Carter received great increases in payouts.

Young people, who in record numbers didn't vote at all soon received the honor of paying more in Social Security taxes. And they had their future potential pay-outs reduced to a tiny fraction of what the current seniors will receive. That is still the system.

The largest single tax the average individual pays is the Social Security tax. You pay 7.5% of your wages and your company pays another 7.5% that it would have paid you in wages but must instead be sent to the Federal Government.

Those of us who are self-employed do the same thing only we don't have any delusions about who's paying for the second 7.5 % like most employees. The total for each worker is over 15%. It's scheduled to go even higher. And, unlike Federal income taxes, there are no offsetting deductions such as home interest rates or charitable contributions for the Social Security tax.

It's important that you realize that when Senator Moynihan and others in power proudly uphold the so-called Social Security surplus trust fund as an example of their responsible actions all they are showing you is your future obligation to pay for more debt. The dollars supposedly deposited into the trust fund to pay future Social Security benefits have all been lent back to the Congress to pay current government employees and all the other debts they owe. If you look at the most optimistic official Federal Government projections, (some are in my chapter on the budget) the debts of the Federal Republic will never be repaid.

All the Social Security trust fund owns is a promissory note from an entity that can never repay the debt. Everywhere else in the world, except in the minds of the majority of our elected officials, the definition for this condition is insolvency. If a person's only asset is a promissory note that can never be collected, they are by definition insolvent. It is axiomatic. The plan Senator Moynihan is so proud of is a fantasy. I suppose this makes Senator Moynihan the Phantom of the Congress. I predict Senator Daniel Patrick Moynihan's famous 'Death Wish' warning to George Bush or to anyone else who wants to change the Social Security system will be his own political epitaph once Democracy is accomplished.

I have made a few easy calculations regarding payments to Social Security. Here's just one example of something the citizens could decide once you become sovereign: Instead of the Social Security system being controlled by the five hundred and forty-five lawmakers via their political appointees, it should be turned over and managed by the National Association of Securities Dealers (NASD) member firms. Instead of a communal pool of money to award faithful voters, every person would have their own insured account.

Through the Securities Investment Protection Corporation (SIPC) each account would be insured, and the premiums paid out of the operating budgets of the firms themselves--just like any existing account at any investment house. The Federal Government could offer an extra umbrella policy on Social Security accounts for the fearful.

Licensed and bonded professional portfolio managers (i.e. Mutual Funds) would manage the Social Security retirement accounts in virtually the same way and with the same options that they already offer for IRAs and private pensions.

For example, a 35 year-old woman now earning $35,000 per year adjusted annually for inflation making annual payments of 15% to her own S.S. account, and based upon an average U.S. Growth Fund track record of the past twenty years, could reasonably expect to have $1,000,000 in her account within twenty years. This in addition to any other private retirement plans such as IRAs or Pensions. Look up growth Mutual Funds and multiply it out yourself.

This is a realistic projection based upon the average track records of the results of domestic growth funds. The anti-Democracy forces will point out that there is risk involved and the results aren't guaranteed. But the alternative is the existing system. This same 35 year-old woman will have to work at least 30 more years (ten more than in my example above) and the Social Security system as currently forecast won't even pay her back as much principal as she will have by then contributed, much less pay back the loss of earnings she could have had on her principal investment. If you want to have the same guarantee that Social Security now gives you it could be an option. But with that option you will have to be willing to settle for a tiny fraction of what you would otherwise have under the plan I propose.

Why don't we already have this system now? The five hundred and forty-five lawmakers would have to give up control. They would have nothing with which to buy the votes of Seniors. As I've described below and in the chapter on Income Taxes and illustrated in dollars and cents in the chapter on the Budget, under National Democracy the current surplus deposited to the trust fund would be administered and invested (in vested accounts in each working citizen's name) in American industry by the National Association of Securities Dealers. The money in the trust fund would not be lent to Congress to squander.

I am registered and licensed through my Broker Dealer by the National Association of Securities Dealers to advise and direct the investment of, among other funds, the retirement and insurance monies for clients. If I, or any one of my peers in the industry imitated the flagrant disregard for the client's opportunity on their principle investment as those in Congress accept as normal and desirable, we would be put out of business, fined and possibly imprisoned. Those in Congress are immune from Securities and Exchange Commission (SEC) and National Association of Securities Dealers regulations and prosecution because they are sovereign under the Federal Republic. They are, in fact, above the law and they know it.

Currently the news media plays into and supports the government on Social Security. The people in the news media are not trained in finance, business and economics any more than the lawyers in Congress, the White House or the Supreme Court are. The news media also needs crisis and controversy to sell commodities as much as the politicians do to keep our attention and thoughts off the one and only real issue (that we need Democracy.) Is it any wonder that many radio and television personalities end up in political office?

Jesus Christ, as he hung dying on the cross, looked down at the men designated to terminate his life and said, "Father forgive them, for they know not what they do.' Our Nation is dying. It is being bled to death by the federal republicans in power. Personally, I simply find it impossible to believe that those championing the current Social Security System, or any of the other taxes for that matter, don't understand what they've done to the citizens of the Nation.

But if it is true that those in Federal Office have no malice of intent and simply don't know what they are doing, why are you leaving them in power? Either way, the solution is the same. It's time to remove them all from power as the majority of citizens come into agreement long enough to peacefully amend the Constitution to change the government from a Federal Republic to a National Democracy. We can continue debating the issues afterward when we have the power to actually change things to the way we've decided they ought to be.

PRODUCTIVE VS
NON PRODUCTIVE

'Don't bite the hand that feeds you.'

Wise old saying.

Government employees are paid to produce nothing. They exist entirely off of the wealth created by the productive sector which the government siphons off through taxes. Their wages are tied to inflation which the Federal Government deliberately creates by expanding the money supply faster than the growth of the Net Domestic Product (NDP). Few of the employees and workers who actually create value in the productive sector have this benefit. It isn't enough to say that they should have the benefit, of course they should. It's a symptom of the bigger problem. There would be no overall inflation if the growth of the money supply were tied directly to the increase in the Net Domestic Product.

Under Democracy, public employee wages should be set by the majority of voters. I suggest a formula. Government employees should at most earn no more than the average person--regardless of their job. In 1990 the figure was close to $23,000 per year. Another formula would be to tie it to the Net Domestic Product per person. In 1990 this figure was approximately $19,000 per capita. An average of these two would be the most balanced approach.

This formula would, for the very first time, bring the light of reality to every government employee. It would emphasize to everyone that every government employee should have as their foremost concern the citizens they serve, and not just the perpetuation of the government bureaucracy. Every act of every public servant would be founded upon one concept: That of encouraging overall the American society to function better. Certainly the NDP is the most objective and the best measure of the state of the society as a whole.

For the first time we would have public servants instead of public masters. No one, including the President, Senators or Congressmen should earn more than the average American worker according to the final formula above. If the job is more complicated it should be streamlined or contracted out to the private sector who would then have to operate in the black.

If those in power now are unhappy with this amount they have only themselves to blame for overburdening the employees of the productive sector with unnecessary taxation in the first place. If they want a raise they only have to see to it that government is streamlined as I've outlined in the chapters on the Budget and Income Taxes so the Gross Domestic Product can grow vigorously.

In November 1993 the Federal Government announced that it has an additional unfunded liability of one trillion dollars that must be paid to future Federal retirees. Under the current government the Federal lawmakers will have no choice but to either raise your taxes again or borrow another trillion dollars to pay the obligation. The only way you can put a stop this taxation without representation is to change the U.S. Federal Republic to a National Democracy.

Under the National Democracy government employees should have the same opportunity as the average worker to establish their own Individual Retirement Accounts out of their own wages instead of the extravagantly publicly financed pensions they currently enjoy.

GOVERNMENT
VS
PRIVATE SECTOR
HOLIDAYS

Government employees have more paid holidays and higher average wages, benefits and retirement income than anybody else. This is a profound contradiction since they are paid to produce nothing. Under Democracy the voters should change all government holidays to Sunday except for the paid holidays celebrated by the average worker in the productive sector. Those Government employees who want to celebrate and remember the important occasions away from work will have Sunday to do so.

If an individual Government employee believes he or she can and should have more holidays than this plan calls for they should by all means leave Government service and start their own business. Then they can take off any day they want to celebrate at their own expense. If they don't want to serve with a sense of patriotic sacrifice for less income they should not be public servants.

CULTURAL RELATIVISM

'Everything is everything and vice-versa.'

Popular saying at The Evergreen State College in the 1970's.

It is certainly true that North America was inhabited by Native Americans, those of Spanish descent, African American, French, Russian speaking peoples and some Asians in addition to those of English and Western European heritage at the time of the American Revolution. Today every race and ethnic and cultural group lives in relative peace in the United States of America.

In spite of our problems and the divisive laws passed by the five hundred and forty-five lawmakers since our country's inception, ours is the most homogeneous and, relative to all other counties, the most egalitarian and overall prosperous nation on earth. Here, under the law, everyone is deserving and entitled to respect for their person.

Nevertheless, it is a matter of historical fact that as a government the United States of America was founded by Christians. Only in a nation dependant upon Christian principles is freedom as we understand it possible. All our civil, criminal and property laws and what we call ethics are in fact direct applications from the Bible.

Jesus Christ was the first person who ever lived to teach that we should cope with our enemies through peaceful persuasion by loving them and doing good things to them and forgiving those who wrong us. These elements alone translated into a nation's identity allow for unity based upon trust and permit such realities as national commerce to exist.

Jesus was the first to teach a philosophy based upon total brotherhood, equality and liberty. He spoke more eloquently and succinctly about what is and what is not truth and freedom than anyone else who's ever lived. Any one who doubts or denies this simply hasn't studied Jesus Christ's own words and his teachings. His thoughts and principles and interpretations of reality were of such revolutionary import that they transformed the world. Western Civilization and everything we are is the manifestation of His philosophy. Even the concept that all individuals in society should have the freedom to peacefully disagree with this or any other attitude of the majority was first introduced to humanity by Jesus Christ. Before Jesus Christ, all other religious or political philosophers taught that humans should subdue or kill their enemies.

Christians worship God. God is a living Being who created all things. The laws of nature, which God designed, are absolute. All knowledge originates from God, including the realization that energy cannot be destroyed, only changed. The current scientific version of how the universe was created, as promoted by such scientists as Stephen Hawking, is that sub-atomic particles of matter (quarks) simply and spontaneously sprang into existence out of nothing. But, in reality, God created everything out of God's own nature. It's as if God spoke the universe into existence. It makes perfect sense considering God's nature. According to the first chapter of the book of the Apostle John, who recorded much of what Jesus said, God is a conscious Being composed of living love that is made out of light. According to this understanding, it's likely that all particles of matter are composed of photons of light that have been slowed down until they congealed into solid matter.

Jesus called God his Father and was sent to deliver a hopeful message that the totality of life is much more than any of us ever imagined. You have to study Jesus's own words and the rest of the Bible to learn for yourself. If you do you will understand by His example why we Christians celebrate life and not death. Only as a last resort and not even in self-defense, but to preserve the Nation, are Christians allowed by our belief to take drastic action. Open respect for other peoples as persons has only existed and can only exist in societies where the truth about Jesus Christ is lovingly taught and accepted by the mass of the population.

This is all common sense to anyone with wisdom. In our public schools common sense was ruled out of fashion by order of the Supreme Court and a majority of the five hundred and forty-five lawmakers. The Constitution doesn't prohibit prayer or the teaching of the Bible in school. It only says that the Federal Government shouldn't establish an official State religion. If you don't believe me read the document for yourself. Even the phrase, 'Separation of Church and State' is a recent interpretation of the Supreme Court.

For thirty years the moral teachings of the Bible have been prohibited in public schools. See the result for yourself. Pick up today's newspaper. Somewhere in your own city or a city near you a young man has shot to death another man or women or child. And for no other reason than that the criminal felt insulted by the victim's presence. No real reason! And that's the point. Reason has failed in our society.

In spite of what the five hundred and forty-five lawmakers are telling us, poverty isn't causing this explosion in crime. Proponents of Cultural relativism who now control the Federal government and public school curriculum officially maintain that all philosophies and 'lifestyles' have the same legitimacy. In reality they only have one real agenda and that is to eradicate Christianity. Their 'successes' can be objectively measured. People in the Depression of the nineteen thirties didn't resort to crime in alarming numbers even though there were many who starved to death. It's not racism either. There are no legal barriers to employment or education in this nation in spite of the five hundred and forty-five's continuing attempts to ferment hate groups so as to divide us into voting camps. The only explanation for these social atrocities and breakdown of leadership is the absence of Christian values and history being taught and embraced by those who embraced Cultural Relativism in our schools and other public institutions.

Democratic values can only exist in a nation where most of the inhabitants practice Christian principles. Cultural Relativism alone is why the social fabric of our society is disintegrating. Over the last thirty years, those being educated in the public schools haven't been set free by the Supreme Court rulings. They've been abandoned. If we are to survive as a people we must remove those now in government from exercising sovereign power. Americans must be sovereign or there will soon be no Nation.

Once you come to realize that all our laws and ethics are in fact expressions of Judeo-Christian principles, you may also realize that the phrase, 'Government can't regulate morality,' is an expression of total confusion. Not only can government regulate morality, but since all our laws are based directly upon these principles, regulating morality is, in fact, the only legitimate function of government.

How many examples like the false reports of Pepsi syringe product tampering and the attack on Nancy Kerrigan the Olympic figure skater have to happen before the leaders of our nation admit the connection between the wholesale abandonment of Christian values and the disintegration of the moral fabric of our society?

After Democracy is created, the citizens themselves will see to it that truth, respect, honor and virtue will again be part of our schools and our government.

EDUCATION

'If the people will lead, the leaders will follow.'

Jeff Merkeley -- Futurist

After Democracy all of the current problems associated with education will end. Thirty years from now, that future generation will look back at this time and at their barbarously ignorant parents in uncomprehending wonder at how Americans allowed education to become such a catastrophe.

There is no agreement about education in the United States. Americans are being deliberately pitted against one another by those in Washington D.C. and their counterparts in State and City government for one reason. That reason is to take our attention off of the real issue, the absence of citizen control over the schools. As with all the other problems of the Republic there is only one viable solution: Democracy.

There is today a funding parity between rural, suburban and inner city schools. Money is not the issue. Racism is also not the issue. I deal with the issue of racism separately under the chapters on that subject and in the one on welfare.

The inner city public schools have been the place where the five hundred and forty-five social experimenters have had the freest hand. What have been the universal results? The schools have been the places of the greatest educational and social disaster. This topic has almost no end when viewed from the problems created by the majority of the five hundred forty-five Federal lawmakers.

Democracy should begin with the complete elimination of the Federal Department of Education. At best this department is a vehicle for political patronage appointments. It needlessly duplicates individual State functions. At worst the department is an agent of anti-Christian anti-Democratic revisionism and serves only to promote the majority of the lawmakers' march toward totalitarian rule by intimidation and thought control of the young.

After the Constitution is amended, Democracy will sweep across the Land. The the anti-Democracy forces who rule our states, counties, city governments, and even school districts will be peacefully swept from power forever along with all their divisive nonsense and anti-Christian drivel. Rational law-abiding parents and teachers within each school district will be able to, for the first time, carry out what they know will work for them.

There will be all kinds of direct ramifications among them: Our children will become well-educated. Schools will not be battle grounds. There will be increased funding and broader choices of curriculum for students as local budgets for schools will most certainly be doubled or tripled by empowered citizens. The ratios of teachers to students will become one to ten or less. I cover some of the other aspects in other chapters.

ANTI-CHRISTIAN REVISION

Americans need the unique Christian principles of forgiveness and respect for other human life to be taught in public schools if for no other reason than that quarreling children need to learn to forgive one anther while they are still at the disagreement stage, before it erupts into physical violence, gun play, bloodshed and death. Haven't we seen enough of what the five hundred and forty-five lawmakers have wrought in our schools? It is the same community where they have had the most impact with their other vote-buying experiments.

Can one person, other than those who are being paid to administer the programs, deny the absolute abject failure of the anti-Christian vote-buying 'reforms' of the last thirty years? Those closest to the five hundred and forty-five who are paid to administer the programs are so adamant in defending the failed strategy that they only serve to convince us that they would say anything and tell any lie if they were paid the same money.

When the Communists came to power in Russia and China the first thing they did was to rewrite their history books specifically to reflect their anti-Christian vendetta. They were utterly ruthless in forcing their new ideology down the throats of their own citizens. But nowhere was this done more cynically than in the schools. In the process of *re-educating* the politically incorrect they eventually murdered tens of millions of their own people. Likewise by their own admissions the Nazis in Germany came to power to replace all ideologies and beliefs with their own. Although Jews became their main target, Christians were ridiculed as weak and cowardly for advocating such *absurdities* as Jesus' command to love and forgive your enemies and do good things for them. If you don't believe this read any of the writings by or about infamous Communists or Nazis.

The more money and experimentation that the anti-Democracy forces have foisted upon our public schools the higher the drop-out rate has been. We're reaping in urban gangs and violence and lawlessness what has been sown for the last thirty years by the federal republicans. Our nation won't survive another thirty years as a place for people to live unless we act now to create a Democracy.

WHO'S VERSION OF GOD?

The issue isn't whose version of reality or God or Christianity should or shouldn't be taught in public schools. The issue boils down to the very definition of what it means to be a person. This definition isn't just for those here in America but for everyone everywhere for all times. It is precisely what the five hundred and forty-five lawmakers can't bear to have you and your children examine from the Christian perspective because it means an end to their rule and way of life. Christians alone know that our rights come from God and not the government.

The federal republicans are against Christian principles for the same reason Joseph Stalin, Adolph Hitler, socialists, communists and all dictators, whatever their name or epic, were against Christ. **It is empowering to be a Christian!**

Jesus was the original author of the definition of true freedom. If you read all His words as recorded in the New Testament and the effect he had on the people who followed him (and not someone else's distorted version) you will discover for yourself that Jesus is freedom personified. He said, 'Blessed are the teachable for they shall inherit the earth.' If you want to inherit the earth open your heart and mind to what Jesus had to say.

The United States of America was founded in the midst of war as the culmination of the wisdom of seventeen hundred years of struggle to create the perfect Christian society (if that were possible). Nothing less. The Founders sought to create a society based on the 'ideals' of Democracy. The Republic was a compromise. To not let the public schools teach at least this much and what those principles are is nothing less than censorship and oppression. Under Democracy, free from the divisive interference of the five hundred and forty-five lawmakers, the citizens can reintroduce young Americans to their heritage.

ACCOUNTABILITY

'You snakes! You brood of vipers!
How will you escape being condemned to hell?'

Jesus Christ

Jesus Christ said the words above to the lawyers of his day. They were the priests who ruled over the Jewish people. Jesus didn't waste time or words. In the New Testament book of Matthew chapter 23, in what today is referred to as the 'Seven Woes', Jesus let the lawyers hear exactly what he thought of their corruption and hypocrisy. If He were here today in the flesh, Jesus could repeat the same speech to the five hundred and forty-five lawmakers ruling our Nation. It's as if the speech were composed for them.

I especially like verse 28, 'In the same way, on the outside you (lawyers) appear to people as righteous but on the inside you are full of hypocrisy and wickedness'. Of course, the lawyers arranged to have Jesus executed for his insight into their character. As an act of mercy and love and to build the faith of nonbelievers, Jesus came back to life. The whole story is in the New Testament.

After Democracy is realized, the United States will still have a President, Congress and Supreme Court--but in an advisory capacity only. The citizens may very well eventually invent a way for Democracy to function without a Congress. Sooner than later the voters may implement the changes I suggest in my chapter on lawyers. If that happens the five hundred and forty-five lawyers will be in the same relative position as a King's noblemen after the republics were created in Europe. After a lifetime of training for their positions, the five hundred and forty-five will have no readily marketable skills outside of their current capacity.

In any event, after Democracy, members of Congress should live and work in the District and State they represent, not concentrated in Washington D.C.. They should spend time soliciting opinions from the citizens and encouraging voter turnout. They should each be provided with a local office, phones, a car, a computer, fax and no more than two assistants. They will be forever free from the burden of talking to lobbyists, PACs and special interests. It will be a much more practical employment of their time and the citizens' money. Such a change will send them as well as the rest of the world the clear message that Americans are running their own country and national affairs for the first time.

Since the five hundred and forty-five have rarely if ever punished their own members, the citizens may very well hold certain individuals in that group criminally liable for the trillions of dollars that have been looted and squandered.

Based upon their actions, the five hundred and forty-five are collectively no different than Charles Keating, Jr. or Michael Milken except that they are currently sovereign over us. Charles Keating Jr. was tried and convicted of mismanaging billions of dollars of Lincoln Savings depositors' money. At his trial, Mr. Keating maintained that each act he committed was legal. Perhaps they were but a jury found that all the transactions taken together and combined with his intent, were criminal. He is expected to be in prison for a long time. Mr. Milken had a similar fate and, though now free from prison, is banned forever from the securities industry. Similarly, Congress and the President have squandered trillions of dollars of the citizen's money. This is what a trillion dollars looks like spelled out: $1,000,000,000,000.

After Democracy the sovereign voters may come to the same conclusions as the jury in the Keating trial and take appropriate action. Don't be surprised after the citizens vote for Democracy if dozens of the five hundred and forty-five suddenly disappear and are later found seeking political asylum in other countries.

They know all too well that they are in fact above about the current laws in terms of accountability. Other wise, hundreds of current and former House members would be now serving prison terms for the House Banking scandal including the Speaker.

The Capitol building in Washington D.C., as in other countries where monarches or other despots are removed, might become a museum as a testimony against the former government if the citizens want it. Personally I recommend it. It is self-evident that placing the five hundred and forty-five lawmakers together only encourages and perpetuates the problems. Except for the President and Supreme Court members, they should live and work exclusively in their home districts.

After Democracy is realized, former elected officials, cabinet officers and government leaders of any rank who have received millions of dollars in payment for selling influence before or after leaving office may also be subject to trial if the voters decide to exercise their sovereign power.

Unpleasant as these thoughts may be to those now in office, it is likely that it may be the only method to convince the lobbyists and special interests as well as the politicians that the citizens of the United States are indeed sovereign and that America is finally, as Ross Perot dreams, 'Not for sale at any price'.

LAWYERS

*'Organized crime never had a chance to get
established in America because the lawyers
in government already had a monopoly on it.'*

John Pepka

The Founders believed it was self-evident that the task of protecting the Nation from invaders was too important to be left to the military alone. That's why they designed a government wherein the civilians controlled the military.

Today it is just as clear that the laws of the United States of America are far too important to be left to the lawyers. Americans should maintain citizen control over the legal system, and they should begin by obtaining sovereignty over the three branches of government by proclaiming Democracy, as outlined in this book.

Whatever official explanation is given by the apologists, the current American legal system revolves around the axiom of situational ethics. To the lawyers, whatever enhances the client's positions is morally correct. Whatever diminishes the client's position is morally incorrect. Common sense tells us that this formula is also the mold for a sociopathic personality. It is a tragedy of our times that the lawyers whose personalities are most adapted to twisting or omitting the truth hold us, the people, hostage.

Look at any attorney in public office at any level of government. It took me forty years to realize that under the Federal Republic those who can not (or care not) to distinguish between the truth and a lie become the most powerful politicians. Under the existing government, the chronicle of corruption, waste and self-excuse is beyond measure. It will never end unless the citizens change the government to a Democracy wherein the voters are sovereign.

Americans must put an end to the teaching of situational ethics in the law schools of the Nation. The practice must end in government, courts and our business community. After Democracy the citizens should intervene and order lawyers, as part of their ongoing practice, to swear to tell and represent the truth, the whole truth and nothing but the truth.

Clients should be told by the lawyers they hire that the latter will represent the truth first and last even if this goes against the interests of the clients. The courts of law need to become courts of truth and justice for a change. In court, lawyers should have to take an oath to tell the truth just like the witnesses and be held in contempt if they refuse. Lawyers should have to take an oath as part of their profession to tell the truth just as medical doctors are sworn never to use their knowledge to deliberately take a life. It hasn't stopped the abortionists but it's a good idea that's failed in medical practice only recently and in that particular circumstance for lack of legal enforcement by the American Medical Association.

As I have stated before, it is impossible for me to write about any subject without seeing it from a Christian perspective. Remember what Jesus had to say about the 'Keepers of the law' or the lawyers of his day? 'You brood of vipers!' 'Woe to you lawyers. You load men down with heavy burdens yet you yourself aren't willing to lift a finger to help them.'

Whether you agree with me or are a lawyer and disagree, the point is the way things are now, as individuals, the citizens of our country have no means to get the real issues out for a vote. Americans deserve better lawmakers than those who can only tell the truth by accident. I trust in the collective wisdom of the two hundred sixty million Americans infinitely more than that of the five hundred and forty-five lawmakers.

After democracy, I can live with any decision of the majority because I know that if it is wrong the majority will recognize it and correct it. As things stand now under the Republic, there is simply no way to change anything. But after Democracy the citizens should at least for a time consider placing a moratorium on allowing lawyers to serve in public office. Most of the current five hundred and forty-five would have to go! It would be wonderful. The Nation could start anew with a clean sweep by taking over the American Bar Association long enough to rewrite its charter and conditions for membership and disbarment.

The majority will have the power to inaugurate Democracy with citizen leaders instead of the old gaggle of sociopathic liars. The ban could exclude any practicing lawyers and anyone who's ever attended law school until the next generation of lawyers raised up under the new ethics of Democracy are proven ready to practice as the servants of the public. The existing crop of lawyers would still be around to give opinions, just as the generals are available to advise the President and carry out the Commander-In-Chief's orders. But that's all the power they would have.

And finally, as Americans who are about to become sovereign over our own country, we must never again allow the lawyers to have the final word over what is or is not the law of our Nation.

ABORTION

Believe it or not, there are several perfectly eloquent solutions to satisfy all parties regarding the issue of abortion. All that is needed for them to be revealed and implemented is a political reality in which Americans are sovereign over the government (the opposite of now) and in which the five hundred and forty-five lawmakers can no longer divide us. It is true that the lack of rational leadership by men in our Nation's highest offices encourages the same lack in men in general.

For every woman who gets an abortion there is a man who is equally responsible for getting her pregnant in the first place; a man who has not only abandoned the woman but the child inside her. There are rare exceptions but in the main I've always believed that the most cowardly act that a man can commit is to abandon his children. Men who do this are despicable.

The cowards who say, 'I'm not responsible,' are echoing the example of the likes of the men in high authority. What other choice do women have but to echo, 'I'm not responsible'? The notion that women are somehow empowered by taking the life of their own children is a symptom of the degree to which they've been abandoned by the despicable and cowardly men who acted so irresponsibly. It is one of the most horrible tragedies of our age that men in government voice agreement with the ruling which legalized the slaughter of helpless and innocent children in this way. The last twenty years of slaughter has proven to even the most casual observer of the American scene that U.S. women were not in any way empowered by Roe vs. Wade. They were abandoned.

I know from many years of training as a peer-counselor that women who choose abortion are having one message shouted into their ears by the Feminists, 'women's rights, power etc.' but they are feeling something all together different in their hearts. Women who are pregnant use words to describe the baby inside of them that the political activists don't seem to understand. But my conclusions are for men because women as a group are now facing the hardest decision they will ever have to make with the advent of the RU 486 abortion pill.

I believe that any man who abandons or encourages a women he has impregnated to have an abortion is himself equally responsible for the death of that child.

When males start acting like mature men instead of trying to imitate the pathetic examples in movie action films, television, gang leaders and that of our elected politicians in government, the first people to notice will be the women in their lives. A man with maturity doesn't use a women only for pleasure and then abandon her. Feminists are famous for quoting one line in the New Testament to dismiss all of it: 'Wives obey your husbands.' But if they studied the entire Bible, even the Feminists would discover that men are directed and encouraged to act towards women with the utmost respect, consideration, honor and loyalty as totally equal holders of God's wonderful promises. Every admonishment for women to love, respect and honor men is matched by more than two for men to respect honor and love women.

It is a Christian principle that sexual intercourse be confined to marriage. I believe that every American male (of any age) should honor the female of his sexual desire by abiding by this principle. This includes accepting any child he helps create. Males should be confronted with this ultimatum: Before you have sex get married!

Even if you are a young teenager (especially if you are a young teenager) you must take responsibility for your behavior. Condoms regularly fail even when they are used. They are only one symptom of the real issue: Freedom equals responsibility and there can be no true freedom where adherence to Christian principles is absent.

The problems, costs and moral crisis associated with abortion or with the lack of abstinence before marriage are so enormous that the new government should reclassify it as a public health issue (instead of one of Civil Rights) the way it was before Roe vs. Wade. In a similar but negative way, the homosexuals exercised their political power to change the AIDS epidemic from a public health issue into a civil rights issue to prevent widespread testing. (Read the chapter on Gay Rights). Just look at these two situations together and tally up the results in human deaths if you have the courage. If abortion were again made a public health issue there would be no need for American females to get abortions by the millions every year.

In an earlier draft of this book, I proposed vasectomy as an alternative to abortion but I've since changed my mind. This alternative is worth examining if only to discard its viability. Vasectomy is certainly a less drastic remedy than an abortion or the abortion pill. It's also less expensive and safer than an abortion. I've had a vasectomy and I can attest that it was a minor surgery lasting about twenty minutes. I was awake the whole time and went straight home afterward. The discomfort goes away after a few days. I know of many men who have had the process reversed, some even after decades.

Yet without a universal commitment to Christian standards of morality, dealing with the cause (promiscuous males) instead of the effect (pregnant females) still requires a better solution than what vasectomy alone offers. Vasectomy in itself will do nothing to stop the spread of sexually transmitted diseases. When the Women's Movement is reborn under National Democracy (as described in the chapter on that subject) the majority of females will have the power to demand a higher standard of males. And don't think they won't! A common sense saying from the Bible that fits this discussion is, 'One word of caution to a wise man is worth a thousand blows to the head of a fool.'

Under Democracy, the complex conditions which lead up to the point where each year millions of pregnant American women feel they have no choice other than to abort the child within them would be unraveled and set right. The majority of the citizens will also see to it that neither men nor women without wisdom or honor will be allowed to exercise power over the public.

In spite of everything that Americans can and will do under National Democracy to bring the number of abortions down to a very small percentage of today's count, there will always be a few women who either have no medical choice or because of other circumstances will need to have an abortion. As lamentable as this may be, it is also inevitable. For these women the health providers must provide a safe and affordable way to have this done. No American woman will have to feel abandoned just because she's pregnant. The current hysteria fueling this issue (Pro-choice) must and will only come to an end under National Democracy. At that time the current group of federal republican lawmakers will no longer be able to divide Americans from one another on this issue or any other for their own political gain.

The Bible says that, 'God knew us even before we were conceived in our mother's womb.' Certainly everything necessary for human life is present at the moment of conception. Any one who denies this is either confused or lying. The determination of whether the new life will be male or female is already made. That tiny being is very much alive and I believe aware of her or his existence. If allowed to grow, in a few weeks the tiny person will look very much like what everyone recognizes as human if not very big. But even at the moment of conception the new person is a complete human being.

It breaks my heart every time I read that less than a few percent of abortions are for medical reasons, rape or incest. Most are for birth control. Civilization will not survive if our Nation continues to allow one group of people to be executed merely because they are viewed as inconvenient. Abortion clinics are nothing less than death camps. Since 1970 thirty three million children have already been murdered in the United States alone. In this century the communists did this to tens of millions in both Russian and China and the Nazis did the same in Europe. The excuses don't matter.

Jesus said, 'If your right hand causes you to sin cut it off. Better to enter the Kingdom of Heaven minus a hand than to go into hell with both intact.' Marriage is infinitely better than other possible alternatives. The only realistic solution is that as a people and as a Nation we must change and become what God intended us to be. For males who want to mature and become complete men, study the words of Jesus as well as the rest of the Bible, especially the New Testament. Ask to be filled with the Spirit of God as Jesus described. You will discover that only directly through God can you become what you've always wanted to be and find the satisfaction you are looking for elsewhere.

It's worth observing that the T.V. advertising campaign that Mr. Clinton and Health and Human Services Secrary Donna Shalala launched in January of 1994 to promote the sale of condoms is just another government farce intended to take your attention off of the real issues. The 'official' goal of the T.V. blitz is to stop or slow down the rate of sexually transmitted diseases and unplanned pregnancies. Yet, it was perfectly timed to take your attention off of the mid-December 1993 admissions by Arkansas State Troopers that they were regularly instructed to solicit and arrange adulterous sexual encounters for the then governor and even president-elect Clinton (he's never denied the allegations). But sexual immorality, Mr. Clinton would now have us believe, is not fornication or adultery but 'Did you wear a condom?' The commercials are being funded with borrowed money that those of you in the productive sector will have to repay.

Men must demand of all other males that they grow up and become mature men, which by definition includes the adoption of responsible Christian standards of behavior. *The majority in our society does have the right to demand higher standards of personal responsibility from every citizen including the President.* Those who don't believe this are confused and have the current batch of lawmakers as well as those from the past two decades to blame for deliberately misleading them.

Under National Democracy, the wisdom of the majority of Americans will resolve all the problems Mr. Clinton and the other elected federal republicans created or refused to face. Including these.

SPECIAL INTERESTS, POLITICAL ACTION COMMITTEES AND FOREIGN LOBBYISTS

In his Gettysburg Address, Abraham Lincoln said, among other things, '...a nation of the people, for the people, and by the people...' Where does he say, '...a nation of the special interests, for the lobbyists, and foreign corporations'?

Mid-level bankers in Italy, Mexico or Japan, who have never set foot on United States soil, have much more influence in America than individual American citizens. This contradiction has come about because there are only five hundred and forty-five lawmakers trying to do the thinking for two hundred sixty million American citizens.

The emergence of large special interests and lobby groups is a symptom of this contradiction. It is estimated that there are eighty thousand full-time lobbyists buying influence in Washington D.C. Not one of them represents me and I'll wager they don't represent you either. Not one of them is pro-Democracy. Read Ross Perot's book, 'Not For Sale At Any Price,' for more information.

Under Democracy, the Special Interests, PACs and foreign lobbyists should have to make their appeals directly to the American citizens via newspaper and television commercials just like anyone else who wants your money or your cooperation. It should be a felony or perhaps even treasonous for any Federal office holder to take money from a special interest now or when they leave office. Once Americans create a Democracy and are sovereign they will decide.

SAFE STREETS

AND CAPITAL PUNISHMENT

'As a people we must strive to give up our hate, fear and guilt. These feelings only serve to paralyze us from taking action. The results for our Nation will be justice for all sure and swift.'

The Author

Racism is not the cause of the horrifying increase in violence in America in spite of the avalanche of excuses coming from Washington D.C. and many of the African American leaders. (Refer to chapter on racism.)

Economic denial, institutionalized poverty and arbitrary social and legal exclusion characterize the systematic oppression of one group by another. As lamentable as these conditions are, together they are not at the root cause of the deadly violence and senseless crime that's being played out daily in American cities.

If this type of systematic oppression were the root cause of lawlessness and violence, our courts, jails and prisons would be overflowing with the most oppressed group in our nation: They would be flooded totally beyond bursting with women. Not men.

In the great Depression of the 1930's the unemployment rate was much higher than today. The lives of the average person were much worse off than the so called poverty-stricken today. Lack of food, medical attention and economic opportunity was much worse in the 1930's than today.

Yet, there was no general increase in lawlessness nor were there uncontrolled crime waves. Young people didn't organize themselves into gangs to terrorize their neighbors in cities and surrounding communities. I used to work for the Criminal Justice

System, first in evaluation, then in planning and I know something about the subject.

According to every study I've read, the one determining factor that transcends all economic classes, race and income factors to predict whether a young person will get involved in crime, drugs, have an abortion or drop out of school is whether or not that child grows up with a father in the home in addition to a mother. The difference today boils down to a lack of leadership from the top on down.

Three decades have passed since young women began to be paid to have as many babies as they could but only if they didn't get married and didn't live with the fathers. What a burden it must be for the five hundred and forty-five detractors of common sense to cope with what they have done. If only they could be shocked.

Recidivism means a return to crime. It means a person, once they are arrested, tried and convicted and punished, upon release commits the same kind of crime thus beginning the same cycle again. For thirty years, experts hired at the citizen's expense by the five hundred and forty-five, have maintained that capital punishment is not a deterrent to crime. Yet the vast numbers of violent crimes, murders, rapes, assault and drug crimes are being committed by the same people over and over again. It is an undeniable fact that capital punishment ends recidivism for the person who is executed.

There are a large number of people, especially in political office who criticize Christians and Jews for advocating the death penalty. They point out that capital punishment violates the Ten Commandments. The Ten Commandments were given to Moses and recorded in the book of Exodus of the Bible. I recommend that the critics read the rest of the book of Exodus and the rest of the Bible and the New Testament. The Ten Commandments are only the first ten. When and why to execute habitual criminals is spelled out on the next pages with the other laws given by Moses. It's perfectly clear in context that 'Thou shall not kill,' means 'Do not commit murder.' When Ted Bundy was executed, it was justice, not murder. One of his victims was a young women who attended the small college I also attended. I saw her the day before she was reported missing after a film on campus. She was an innocent person guilty only of accepting a ride with Bundy. As a parent, I'm glad Ted Bundy can never be released on parole. He earned his punishment.

Personally, I believe that the five hundred and forty-five lawmakers don't want capital punishment in this country because it is all to easy for them to see that the end of the Republic is near. Perhaps they don't want to be tried and convicted of treasonous mismanagement and executed by the coming new government.

Under Democracy the majority of voters could summarily order that anyone convicted of one count of first degree murder be imprisoned. Any one convicted of two counts could be executed. Anyone currently awaiting execution on death row could be put to death within ninety days with no more appeals. They might also decree that a person convicted of one count of first degree rape could be automatically sentenced to prison. Anyone convicted of two counts could be ordered castrated. Any one convicted of three counts could be executed.

Once sovereign, the citizens could order capital punishment for any type of serious crime. Drug dealers, child pornographers, habitual sex offenders and any other violent crime the voters designate as beyond redemption could be speedily tried, convicted and executed. Every gang member could be prosecuted and convicted on conspiracy charges if even one of their members commits a serious crime. The gangbanger's way of life could come to an end under Democracy.

The current system designed by the five hundred and forty-five doesn't work. Criminals who were convicted and sentenced to multiple life sentences in the past, when Capital punishment was ruled cruel and unusual, could be summarily ordered to be executed by the majority of voters. When the citizens are sovereign the wisdom of the majority will become the law.

Serial rapists often become serial killers upon release from prison. I'm sure that two hundred sixty million Americans possess the collective wisdom to know what exemptions to make and for whom. If the citizens make mistakes ruling ourselves through Democracy, and we will, they will be our mistakes and not the mistakes of the five hundred and forty-five lawmakers currently ruling us.

In the chapter on the Second and Fourth Amendments, I write more about this issue but it has become apparent to me that the gangs in the cities are being deliberately nurtured and allowed to continue by the federal republicans to terrorize the citizens. The gangbangers are in effect State-sponsored terrorists. The goal of the majority of the five hundred and forty-five lawmakers and their counterparts in State and City government is to allow the atrocities to continue and grow until the law abiding citizens themselves ask to give up their Second and Fourth Amendment rights voluntarily.

All of the local law enforcement agencies agree that they could put an end to gang violence and activities in a few months but they are being held back by the politicians. It's time for Americans to put an end to such despicable duplicity on the part of the elected officials by changing the Federal, State and Local governments to Democracies.

FAIRNESS IN BROADCASTING

The official news of the ex-Soviet Union was printed in a newspaper called '*Pravda*'. In the Russian language, 'pravda' literally means 'truth'. The few hundred men who ruled the ex-Soviet Union decided what balance of 'facts' and opinions could be released and what could not. The citizens of the USSR had no First Amendment rights. Today there is no Soviet Union and Pravda is a muck-raking rag modeled upon western tabloids.

In August 1993, the Democrats in the House of Representatives of the Federal Republic of the United States of America introduced legislation that's being commonly referred to as the 'Fairness Doctrine'. The underlying political intent of their legislation is to nullify the First Amendment freedom of speech rights of eight or nine national radio broadcast journalists who are not in lockstep agreement with the U.S. lawmakers' totalitarian agenda.

It's worth noting that out of all the hundreds of national radio and television personalities in U.S. news and current affairs that only these few are in even slight disagreement with the majority of the five hundred and forty-five lawmakers. Their differences with the existing government are minor compared to my own. Not one of them has ever advocated changing the government as I have. None of them has suggested a completely new way to fund government as I have in the chapters on income tax and the budget.

Yet just the existence of these broadcasters and their willingness to quibble over fairly minor issues via the public airways has caused them to be perceived as a serious threat to the current lawmakers. Much of the struggle is over whether the maximum personal income tax rate should have been left where it was at 32% or raised to 36% under President Clinton's and the Democrat's plan. (Passed into law in August 1993.)

I'm not surprised by anything they do anymore, but the lawmakers attempts to further restrict First Amendment rights has re-emphasized your need for your Second Amendment rights. (Refer to the chapter on that subject.) By introducing such legislation the lawmakers have confirmed their underlying intentions. Their act is just another signal that the five hundred and forty-five know the end is coming for their form of government and they are trying to do whatever they can to forestall the inevitable.

Without question the most famous of these radio journalists is Rush Limbaugh. Mr. Limbaugh is by his own admission a late bloomer in American partisan politics. In prior decades apparently he was a top 40 radio disk jockey and a sports announcer. He is the loudest if not the official voice of the Republican party. Mr. Limbaugh also has two best selling books. There's no business like show business unless of course it's politics. As was the case with Ronald Reagan, Rush Limbaugh also gives you both. I've listened to him almost daily since 1991. Personally, I think his rock & roll parodies of President Clinton are hilarious and well deserved. I especially enjoy his coverage of the issues as well as his humor and wit.

Mr. Limbaugh accurately reflects the frustrations most rank and file Republicans have felt for decades. Thousands write, fax or send him e-mail with 'mega didos' of appreciation. The effect is that he often takes credit for the 'new' insights and has proclaimed himself a 'Talent on loan from God'. At those moments his style of braggadocio seems to be borrowed from 'championship' T.V. wrestlers. That's usually when I turn him off. Obviously, based upon my own conclusions written in this book, I think his analysis and conclusions are incomplete but overall Mr. Limbaugh offers the only national daily alternative view into the affairs of the nation that the Democrats who control the mainstream news media choose to ignore. His serious presentations of the issues are refreshing and often brilliant. I hope he never leaves the airwaves.

If you consider that the entire Federal bureaucracy is nothing less than an extension of the Democrat Party and that it is now successfully being used to stifle the voices of even minor dissenters, such as Mr. Limbaugh, then you must conclude that the U.S. government has in fact become a totalitarian state.

I believe that all issues related to broadcasting should be left for you the citizens to decide once you are sovereign under the coming National Democracy and not to the current lawmakers of the lame duck Federal Republic. Future historians will write about the lawmakers of this time. They will undoubtedly compare the relative closeness in time of the end of the Soviet Union with the end of the U.S. Federal Republic. In comparison it will be said that federal republican 'fairness' equaled communist 'pravda'.

MOSCOW

*"Let us be willing to remold society
by redefining what it means to be a human being."*

Hillary Rodham Clinton

As quoted by Anna Quindlen, columnist with the New York Times,
reprinted in the Seattle Post-Intelligencer, October 20, 1993.

In the industrial age all advocates of totalitarian rule have rejected the definition of human nature as laid out in the Bible.

With the ever increasing allegations regarding the Clinton's adulterous marriage does anyone wonder why they are countering, not with denials, but with federally funded T.V. advertising to redefine sexual immorality not as adultery, fornication, homosexual or lesbian sex but with *did you wear a condom?* Does anyone still wonder why the current administration is advocating that the legal number of genders be redefined to include male, female, lesbian and homosexual? The homosexual and lesbian political activists were the largest single financial and most active supporters of the Clinton's 1992 run for the White House.

Who and what the Clinton's are is inexplicable to most Americans. You don't want to believe the worst of your president. It's understandable. Yet we've seen all this before. And the worst is yet to come.

The four-year college I attended as a junior and senior was The Evergreen State College in Olympia, Washington (location of the State Capital). I graduated in 1975. I went there because the school offered a year-long intensive course on global economics. In addition to a Bachelor of Arts, Evergreen offers a graduate degree but only in Masters of Public Administration. I did not know it then, but the school became and still is a national political training and staging center for homosexuals and lesbians planning to enter all levels of government service. It has an international reputation among the gay community.

In the 1970's the gays at that school, who were mostly middle class and wealthy, and the communists (also wealthy by my childhood standards) all seemed ridiculous to a person like me. There I was, from a poor childhood, and one who had left the trades (manual labor) only after getting hurt. I wanted to get a good job (and a safe one) by studying economics and business. I was also mesmerized by the way people make decisions.

As I learned, global economics included the study of not only the nuances of western capitalism but feudal and communist economies as well. Whatever the problems our country had, I didn't understand or appreciate the teachers or the young people's enthusiasm for communism, especially since communism was failing so miserably to enrich its own people. I was openly and publicly denounced by several of them on a regular basis in the classroom and in the other areas of the school for being a 'Capitalist Reactionary.' In retaliation, I would tell the marijuana Marxists such things as their favorite magazine, 'Ramparts' was on a parallel with, 'National Lampoon'. I should have left the school, but I was determined not to let them rob me of my chance for education. In spite of the lack of wise leadership in government, I loved and still love my country. It's my home.

What those people didn't know and what I refused to tell them was that from growing up being hungry and cold much of the time, I understood the bottom line, even if they didn't. Most of the children of the middle class and the rich that I met in those days seemed self-obsessed and ridiculous to me, a child of relative scarcity. I understand more about them now. My African American and Asian friends tell me being around most middle class whites is the same for them.

The gays and lesbians were just two other groups. But looking back, I can see that they were also the most politically single-minded and the most ambitious. If you doubt it just look at their incredible political results since then.

Because I needed and was willing to work, I became the business manager of the campus newspaper and later the secretary to the Student Activities Board. At the newspaper, I met privately with every group that wanted to advertise or make announcements in the newspaper.

As the secretary of Student Activities, which distributed all the State money allocated at the student body's own discretion, I met with any group that wanted to open an office or that wanted student funds for whatever project. I was also the budget officer of the very first International Symposium held at Evergreen and wrote a paper about the steps of how I'd raised money on campus for such projects and from whom. It was distributed to the subsequent symposium organizers who came in ever-increasing numbers. Somehow they all found me and I helped them find money and college staff to help them. Every radical persuasion from all over America and the world came to Evergreen to speak or to be trained in an almost unending succession of events.

My job as secretary to the Student Activities Board was to teach student interest groups how to apply for money. I also structured the Student Activities Board meetings and told applicants how long they could speak to the Board members. The Board members themselves decided who got money and how much. In the course of my work I met with all groups including the communists, socialists, homosexuals and lesbians and helped them get money for any number of projects and symposiums. (You would be utterly astonished at how many splinter groups there were within each category.)

By 1975, I was myself working in state government in the same city as part of a joint Federal, State and Local crime control project. Our two committees had, as I recall, ten million Federal dollars total to spend every year in Washington State. As a planner, I was in a similar position as before at Evergreen except that I was working for the government as an intern under several levels of managers.

Former students from my small college were everywhere in state government. Because I was not then openly opposed to homosexuality, counting several gays among my acquaintances from school, and because our crime control committee had ten million dollars, I was invited to attend meetings and private lunches or dinners as a potential political ally. Occasionally I attended.

It was during my two years at Evergreen and two in local and state government that I learned the gay community was engaged in even more ambitious plans than the Women's Movement. (Refer to chapter on that topic.) During four years of listening, aiding and abetting, I learned that the agreed upon strategy for gays and lesbians all over the United States was to take over the administration of every organization that could be taken over through alliances and infiltration. It seemed a laughable goal to me at the time, one bordering on absurdity. There were so many conspiracy plans on college campuses in those days being planned by young knuckle-heads who had never even had a job. To me they seemed pathetic but I was being paid by the government to help them as well as every other group that wanted money. Yet, I can only look back today at the gay and lesbian plan in utter astonishment. {I recently met with one of my former social science professors who sadly informed me that the entire social science department has completely degenerated into a indoctrination center for feminist 'fascists' (his words).}

The strategy itself, I learned, was based upon the Communist's model for individuals functioning within a pre-socialist society (Capitalism). Evergreen State College also had communist and socialist adherents in great abundance. Evergreen, apparently like all colleges of the 1970's, in addition to faculty who were avowed communists and socialists, had a recruiter (not officially affiliated with the school) who was taking a select number of students to Mexico, then on to Cuba for training. The students were later brought back via Mexico and returned to campus to be placed in government service. As we had no Rhodes Scholars, apparently no candidates from my school were promising enough to be invited to Moscow.

I knew the recruiter slightly as well as several students who told me they were going to the school for 'revolutionaries' in Cuba. I have also met several people since that time who went to the same school in Cuba who were recruited from colleges on the East Coast at about the same time period.

In 1985, at the ten year reunion of my class, I heard from another former student that the recruiter himself ended up joining the campaign of an unlikely candidate for U.S. Congress who did in fact win the subsequent election. The recruiter accompanied the new Congressman to Washington D.C. and for eight years served on the Congressman's paid staff.

I titled this chapter 'Moscow' in remembrance of the entire series of incidents because, in the Congressman's home district, his name was often preceded by the addition of the word 'Moscow'. When that Congressman left office the recruiter went to work for the successor Congressman from the same district.

I confirmed all this through a former co-worker whose father was a U.S. Senator. The Senator's office investigated it and confirmed that the aide was the same person as the one I knew as the recruiter and that it was true that he was actually on the Congressman's paid staff. They didn't want to do anything about it which is understandable. The last I heard, from the ex-congressman himself, the recruiter still works in Washington D.C. but elsewhere in the bureaucracy.

In the 1950's, Senator Joseph McCarthy made a fool out of himself and his followers, not to mention the damage he brought to thousands of innocent people in his attempts to 'root out' communists in government. That there are spies or subversives in our government and to what extent is an issue of national security and the main concern of the FBI. Based upon the fact that there is no longer a Soviet Union it's evident that, at least in this respect, the seditionists' efforts failed utterly. Still, one wonders how much influence they've had on the thinking of the current batch of lawmakers considering the latter's headlong plunge toward totalitarian rule of the Nation.

Based upon their ideas of 're-inventing' the government presented by Bill Clinton and Al Gore and their fellow Democrats, their strategy would be more aptly called, 'Born again totalitarianism,' or perhaps, 'Brain dead communism.' Yet, I believe it would be very harmful, not to mention futile, for the Citizens to demand an investigation into how many former communist trained spies there are in government. The guilty parties would only deny any wrongdoing and many innocent people would suffer.

I have the same thoughts today about Americans who are being swept away by the Democrat party lawmakers in power as I did in the 1970's about the young people being drawn to communism. At best they were being deluded. At worst there's no crime against being tricked. If someone in authority lies to you it's not your fault. Also, there is no law against stupidity. The best way for Americans to deal with this problem as with every other problem facing us is to make a clean sweep by creating Democracy as soon as possible and take sovereign power away from the current five hundred forty five lawmakers. After that the Citizens can vote whether or not to hold certain existing lawmakers accountable for their individual crimes against the American people as the majority demands it.

POWER

Mao Tse-Tung once declared that 'All power comes from the barrel of a gun.' He was not alone in his view, nor was he far from being accurate. Power is the exercise of control over wealth. All wealth is created directly from material things. There are no exceptions. People get confused because they know, for example, rich doctors. However, their wealth was transferred to them for providing necessary services and not by creating it. The military, education, and medical industries are necessary but they do not add wealth directly or indirectly to the society.

For at least the past thirty years the five hundred and forty-five lawmakers have been engaged exclusively in enhancing their collective power by transferring wealth from productive Americans to themselves and their non-productive political supporters. All the political and social issues and crises of our time have been created or massaged by those in power to facilitate or disguise this one all-consuming activity. It is an understatement to say that the majority of the five hundred and forty-five are power mad.

Yet, it remains that manufacturing is the single most important industry for wealth creation and the one that all the others are directly dependant upon. Without manufacturing, farmers would still be poking holes in the ground with sticks to plant their seeds. People would be living in caves or under the sky. Oil would be just a sticky, smelly black substance. The examples never end.

After Democracy, the citizens of the United States will be free to sort through all the global economic issues and the other issues I outline in this book. They can begin to use their new power to rebuild the basis of wealth creation in the United States abandoned or destroyed by the five hundred and forty-five lawmakers. The more wealthy we are as individuals and as a Nation, the more power we will have. It is essential under the coming National Democracy that the citizens use their sovereign power to prevent those who create wealth from being punished as they are now under the Federal Republic.

Everyone who works in or invests in manufacturing contributes directly to wealth creation. The same is true for agriculture and construction of all kinds. Transportation, communication and information services add value directly to the products that are made or grown by physically making the things made and knowledge of them available to the general population.

The financial service industry adds value indirectly by providing sources of ready investors, insurance and also by providing banking for the means to complete exchanges. All these industries as well as a host of others are required to create wealth. Just how much of these necessary industries the citizens should pay for through taxation is something Americans will be free to debate once they are sovereign.

With NASA as the major exception, those on government payrolls neither create wealth directly nor indirectly. This is true for all transfer payment recipients, including civil servants, those on welfare, military contractors (who by and large produce machines which can never be used for anything directly productive) and those receiving Social Security. They are all paid to produce nothing.

The argument that government employees spend the money they are paid for food, shelter and commodities, and therefore stimulate the economy, serves only to disguise the real issue. They are actually being paid to vote for the majority of the five hundred and forty-five lawmakers in the next election.

If the citizens remove all personal and corporate income taxes and fund the government through the expansion of the money supply as I recommend in the chapters on income tax and the budget, we will have the power instead of the government. There will be ten million new wealth-creating jobs created every year in perpetuity. There will be new jobs for everyone currently on the government payroll who wants to leave government service. The average citizen will have more than enough money to pay for any government services they imagine they've lost as a consequence.

How much government is necessary and what do Americans want to pay for it and how much power government should have and how much we should retain for ourselves are the paramount issues of our age. Once Americans are sovereign they will decide each issue item by item.

Considering the alternatives, what do Americans have to do that's more important than changing the government to Democracy?

MILITARY

The United States needs a strong military to protect its citizens. How much and of what kind is an ongoing subject for debate. This will never end. After Democracy it will be up to the citizens to approve the military budget as well as deciding when to make war and on whom. The president will of course retain all temporary emergency powers.

Perhaps the reason Mr. Clinton wants to cut back at this time is that he may feel the need to prove that he was right to resist military service and demonstrate against his country. Personally, I think the amount being spent to create and support nuclear weapons should be cut by about half and the resources redirected to the development of a manufacturing base between the earth and the moon as I describe below.

Those in the House and Senate know that each civil service job costs three productive sector jobs, and that one military job costs five jobs just as they know that one scientist making weapons of mass destruction costs ten productive sector jobs. But the way they reason, if they cut fifty thousand military jobs, they can create eighty thousand civil service jobs. Government workers are very loyal voters to the Democrats and whether they admit it or not are themselves an extension of the Democrat Party mechanism. Not so those in the military.

In 1989, Ronald Reagan and George Bush as well as the rest of the world were celebrating the collapse of communism in the Soviet Union and Eastern Europe. They and the militarists of the United States claimed that the trillion dollars spent by the United States on nuclear missiles over the past four decades caused the collapse. But all the talk about the 'Peace Keeper' missiles was simply more lies and self-delusion.

I was in Europe for part of 1989. Eastern Europeans and people I've talked to before and after the collapse reported that it was the people themselves who got fed up with communism. They stopped cooperating with the fat and lazy totalitarian government in exactly the same way that I'm suggesting we should with ours. It was the Christians in Europe who led the way to freedom. They got very little press in the United States but, based upon what the Europeans themselves reported, the end of communism had nothing whatsoever to do with the trillion spent on the American nuclear arsenal.

Why is it that since the nineteen sixties the five hundred and forty-five lawmakers have spent trillions of dollars on the military but no enemies have been vanquished? Beginning with John Kennedy but especially with Lyndon Johnson, it's mostly been a great show to distract us while the majority of the five hundred and forty-five lawmakers have looted us.

In spite of all the talk there has been no real cutback in military spending since the end of the Cold War. Are the military's adventures into Central America, Iraq and Africa diversions to give us a reason to think we should continue to spend trillions more on the military? Are these billion dollar skirmishes serving to give us ready hot wars to replace the cold one? Once Democracy is realized, the majority of citizens alone will decide the issue.

Military spending under the Federal Republic has not been about protecting the citizens but about the government using its power to transfer wealth into the hands of special interests who are owed political favors by those in power. Who will ever forget the five hundred dollar hammers or the other hardware sold to the government at a hundred times its original value? Under Democracy the citizens will have to decide what kind of defense to have and how much to pay for the military. I predict it will be even stronger than we have now but without the distraction of opportunists lining their pockets at the tax payer's expense.

After Democracy the voters may decide to have the military actually accomplish something of material value. I hope the citizens order the military to begin using their manpower and resources to build useful things. For example, the Army could test its rocket capacity by placing solar platforms (instead of warheads) high in geosynchronous orbit. These solar platforms could be used to generate electricity to power particle beams or for laser defense systems to repel incoming ICBMs or enemy tanks in the battle field. Except for the actual moment of deterring an enemy attack, the military could project the energy to Earth where it could be used to generate electricity or to convert salt water to fresh. These and other products could be sold.

In time, the military could specialize in energy and might not only offer something productive in return for its staggering cost but it may even begin to pay for itself. Under this scenario, Americans wouldn't need to spend any more than we are now and our military defensive capability would be stronger. We could live in a safer world and get something back in return. Once we are free from the divisive tyranny of the five hundred and forty-five lawmakers and the spider's web of division, deceit and confusion in which they have ensnared us, the possibilities are without limit.

SECOND AND FOURTH
AMENDMENTS

*'How can anyone enter a strong man's house and carry off
his possessions unless he first ties up the strong man?
Then he can rob his house.'*

Jesus Christ -- Matthew 12:29

If you read the Constitution of the United States, which was
signed in 1787 and ratified in 1788, it becomes vividly apparent that
the delegates believed control over the military was far too important
to be left up to the military leaders themselves. The mistakes learned
from their own dealings with England and their study of the past, i.e.
fighting Kings, Emperors and warrior Popes was clear in their minds.

The Founders divided power over the military between the
Legislative and Executive branches thus insuring that the official
representatives of the Republic maintained final control. The
ensuing examples of Napoleon Bonaparte, Adolph Hitler, Joseph
Stalin, Mao Tse-Tung and countless other military despots who
gained control of their own governments then waged war on their
neighbors and enslaved their own people proved to the entire world
the wisdom of instituting Executive and Congressional control over
the military. The new Congress and President together controlled
the Army and Navy and thus could order U.S. forces to repel any
foreign invaders or attack any force hostile to the United States or its
allies.

The Bill of Rights was drafted directly out of the concerns of
the citizens of the individual states of the new Republic. They feared
that the Federal government would have too much power over them.
The First Congress passed these amendments to the Constitution and
forwarded them onto the individual States where they were ratified.
The Bill of Rights went into effect in 1791.

The Second Amendment is the 'Right to keep and bear arms'
by individual citizens plus the right of citizens to form local militia if
they themselves deemed it necessary for self protection. It was self-

evident to them that with the government in charge of the military, individual citizens had to have this right in order to protect themselves from oppression from their own government. They knew and said as much in the preamble to the Bill of Rights, that this was the only way to keep the Federal Government from abusing its command of the United States Army and Navy against its own citizens.

The Fourth Amendment, the 'Right of search and seizure regulated' which protects individuals and property was another example of what they deemed a self-evident right. In this century alone, there may have been as many as one hundred million people in other countries (some estimates are even higher) who were simply seized and murdered by their own governments.

These murders were perfectly legal according to the governments of Nazi Germany, the Soviet Union, Communist China, Cambodia, North Vietnam as well as dozens of nations in Africa. In South America in the Nineteen Seventies, particularly in Brazil, Argentina and Chile (all supposedly Republics) tens of thousands were kidnapped and exterminated without warrants for arrest or trial. Another one hundred million people have died fighting in or as a consequence of the military conflicts perpetrated by those same governments listed above.

The hapless peoples of those countries lacked these two legal rights. As a consequence, they had no legal means individually or collectively to protect themselves from oppression by their own government. Those unfortunates were deemed by their governments to be so politically incorrect that their lives as well as their families, children and even babes in arms were terminated millions at a time.

In this century, only here on the North American continent and in individual nations that acknowledge these basic two rights and in countries that the United States protects through treaties have citizens escaped such a fate.

I've never been there, but I have read that Switzerland has had a continuous form of Republican government for the past eight hundred years. It is the most stable country in the world--not just because Switzerland is hard to invade, but because the people are the most heavily armed. This reality makes it difficult for them to be oppressed by their own government. Most of the billionaires keep their 'safe' money in Swiss banks. It's no coincidence.

For myself, I happen to believe that disputes should be settled peacefully after praying for wisdom from God. If I can't resolve a dispute with someone I turn it over to God. According to my understanding of God's intent, violence is only allowed in defense of the Nation. Our Nation is 'we the people', the two hundred sixty millions of our citizens. The Nation is not just the five hundred and forty-five lawmakers in Washington D.C.

It is clear to me that a form of government-sponsored terrorism has created and nurtured among other groups, the out-of-control gangs in America's inner cities. Americans are asked to be understanding. We understand all too well. I worked in the criminal justice system. I have listened to police officers who say that they could end the gangs' influence in months but they are being stopped by all levels of government, Federal, State and Local.

In December of 1992, while drafting this book, I wrote, 'If Caucasian gangs were let loose in Lincoln, Nebraska, Federal troops would be helicoptered in to obliterate the insurrectionists.' Before I could even begin to edit my notes the Federal Government proved my point in Waco, Texas. The Branch Davidians were originally suspected of just owning automatic weapons. For that they were obliterated to a child.

The actions and the attitudes of the majority of the five hundred and forty-five lawmakers nurtures and encourages crime in the cities. I put it to you that the gangs in the cities are being allowed to exist and are in fact being nurtured by the anti-Democracy forces within the Federal Government. The pathetic handling of the prosecution of the Reginald Denny case (October 1993) as well as the wholesale abandonment of justice against those who rioted, burned property, looted and murdered innocent citizens in the 1992 Los Angeles riots are clear examples of such culpability. The anti-democracy force's aim is to create a condition of confusion and fear where citizens will voluntarily ask give up their Second Amendment rights to bear arms.

In January 1994, Mr. Clinton proposed raising the annual gun dealer licensing fees to $600, nearly ten times higher under the newly enacted Brady gun control legislation. This is a naked move on the govenment's part against your second amendment rights to restrict the supply by persecuting licensed dealers. I've never been a member of the NRA, nor have I ever been a gun dealer, nor ever invested in munitions manufacturing. I've never owned a gun nor any firearm.

I'm telling you objectively that law abiding Americans are being manipulated and exploited in the most cynical way imaginable by the anti-Democracy forces within our own government. Americans aren't deaf, dumb and blind yet under the current government we are in the same position as any hostage. It wouldn't surprise me at all if the year 1994 witnesses the spontaneous creation of thousands of local brigades of citizen run militia to protect themselves from oppression from the U.S. government.

Christian principles have already been stripped away from our Nation by the majority of the five hundred and forty-five lawmakers ruling over us. The last barrier preventing the anti-Democracy forces within the government of the United States from transforming our Nation into an absolute totalitarian state are the weapons in the hand of the law abiding citizens.

After Democracy is established, the majority of citizens will set and direct the agenda for law enforcement. It won't take long before the city streets are safe again.

NUCLEAR POWER

WPPSS
(pronounced, 'Whoops')

I live in Washington State and as every bond trader and bond buyer knows, it is the home of Washington Public Power Supply System (WPPSS for short). WPPSS attempted to build five nuclear power plants here in the mid 1970's to early 1980's. Number Four and Five were the largest municipal bond defaults in history. I believe only one of the five plants ever produced electricity. The rest are mothballed or abandoned-monuments to the politicians' uncontrolled greed and stupidity.

It's worth noting that the citizens of my State were never asked to vote on whether we wanted the plants built here. It goes without saying that tens of thousands of demonstrators (who also happen to be rate payers) protested before construction began.

Since 1978, I have been a licensed securities salesman. In the early to mid 1980's, I was a registered representative of Kidder, Peabody and Co, Inc. My employer happened to be one of the lead underwriters of the last issue of WPPSS.

The last issue of bonds was, as I recall, tax-free, over fourteen percent yield, thirty year, rated AAA that unfortunately may have paid only one dividend before going into default. Believe it or not, I never bought one WPPSS bond for my clients or for myself, even though it meant passing up easy commissions. I didn't participate for the simple reason that I didn't like nuclear power. If the production of electricity with nuclear power is safe, which is debatable, the disposition of the waste on a world wide basis is not.

My mother remembers being told as a young women by the government that if the citizens supported nuclear power the electricity would be so inexpensive and abundant that the meters would be removed from peoples' houses.

When humans discover a safe way to leave the planet, all the radioactive waste from all the nuclear power plants will have to be gathered up and taken off of the planet and hurled into the sun. The

French and the Russians will be forced by the other Nations to retrieve all the millions of steel barrels of radioactive waste they've simply dumped into the ocean.

Washington State was also the home of Dr. Dixie Lee Ray, international proponent of nuclear power, one time chairman of the Atomic Energy Commission, enemy of spotted owls. She was also a former one term Democrat Governor of Washington State. Guess when?

SPACE EXPLORATION

God promised Abraham that his descendants would someday outnumber all the grains of sand on all the sea shores and all the stars in the heavens. I believe it will literally come to pass. Just as I know from reading the Bible and studying history that God judges nations, I also know we are stewards of all we have been given. That responsibility extends to the entire planet, but not in the way that the five hundred and forty-five lawmakers would have us believe.

Sooner than later, the inhabitants of the Earth must move the bulk of our manufacturing base off of the planet if humanity is going to survive much past the next century. I've lived most of my life in the Aerospace Capital of the world. I know Americans can create such a future because I've seen for myself that most of the plans to accomplish this objective have already been drafted by Boeing, NASA and National Space Society scientists. Japan and the European Nations are dedicated to this objective and it's one of the few goals the Russians have carried forward intact from the ex-Soviet Union. We have the means. Americans only lack the national will. National will comes from one source. It boils down to wise leadership.

The work at NASA is the only exception that I can see to the non-productive government spending axioms I've related in this book. The economic rate of return to private industry from the new technology developed by the NASA scientists is seven to one.

Humanity needs more technology, not less, to create wealth without causing pollution. Under Democracy the environmentalists will no longer be divided from other Americans by the five hundred and forty-five lawmakers. We will all be free to see the real solution. If we all hadn't been distracted by the shadow show put on for us over the last thirty years by those wrangling for power, Americans could have already moved some of our industrial base off of the planet.

Anyone who saw the film 2001 when it premiered in 1968 will know that the basic knowledge to create a base on the moon and another between the earth and the moon existed then. Americans need to send people back to the moon to build bases from the bauxite (aluminum) that covers the moon.

From there Americans can construct mass drivers which can be used as simple electric catapults. Mass drivers use the same technology as the high speed trains on earth. Between and around the Earth and the Moon there are five places in space that if an object were placed there it would not drift away nor orbit either celestial body. The pull of the moon and earth are equal in these places. These are the next 'high' frontiers of space.

These are the locations Americans, if we are first, can build floating factories which will, using electricity created from solar power, turn out all that humans consider necessary for life from the natural resources of the moon. If not, the locations will belong to the Japanese, Germans or Russians or whoever is first.

From space, we might use existing designs to build hollow cables of aluminium, and float them like sticks in the water in the earth's atmosphere (called beanstalks). The cable itself could be 'anchored' to a manufactured asteroid in a very high earth orbit. Any one who will desire to leave or return to the planet will be able to do so by riding an elevator propelled by an electric motor and a wheel attached to the cable.

From the materials manufactured in space, this generation of Americans can make anything. We could start by creating giant rotating wheels that would be many miles across in which people could live and work creating new wealth under an open blue sky with lakes and trees and everything humans need and consider beautiful and necessary. All this has already been designed. With much of the manufacturing base transferred off the planet, we could give the future generations an Earth where people can live free from industrial pollution. It would be an environmentalists' utopia.

Within decades, Americans would then have the means to fly to the other planets and asteroids. There are enough raw materials and asteroids within the solar system to sustain exponential economic growth of humanity for a thousand years. With the relatively unlimited natural resources and energy of our solar system, there will be so much real work to do that conditions like unemployment, hunger and poverty will be words to describe a past that will no longer exist. In time the human population will be measured in hundreds of trillions yet nowhere will people have to live in crowded conditions. I believe this is the way God's promise to Abraham will come to pass.

The issues of our time only seem complex because they have been made deliberately so by the five hundred and forty-five lawmakers and their political minions and also because the current problems are viewed from the perspective of the relatively limited natural resources of this planet. Americans must take the lead to move the industrial base off of this planet. Any long-term solutions to problems that remain after National Democracy is realized will have this issue at its core.

There is a constant stream of sub-atomic particles flowing from and around earth's iron core. Electromagnetic particles flow between the magnetic north pole and the magnetic south pole. This is the same force which causes water to drain in the clockwise direction in the northern hemisphere and counter-clockwise in the southern hemisphere. It interfaces with the sun's own field and is called 'solar wind' or solar plasma.

A few scientists believe the field is actually physical and that the sun's field interfacing with the earth's field is actually propelling the earth and all the planets around the sun much like a giant gear turning a smaller one. That would also explain why all the planets rotate around the sun in the same direction and in relative plane. All the planets but one turn on their axis in the same direction and approximately 90% to their orbits.

One day soon, when American scientists have freed their attention from making weapons of mass destruction, perhaps one of them will discover that the magnetic fields are the key to leaving the planet safely. Perhaps humans, or at least cargo, can ride the flowing current off of the planet on vehicles powered by the magnetic flow with engines of electrically charged gyroscopes. I imagine it working liken to a child's toy being propelled up into the air by a water spouting from a hose.

After Democracy, Americans at least, will live in a more rational nation. People won't be afraid to think. The peoples of the other nations of the world will see what we have done and all those who are allowed to will follow suit. To God who gave us our rights, let it not be said of this new generation of Americans that, 'We were afraid, so we hid our talents in the ground.' (nuclear silos) Let us hear instead, 'Well done, good and faithful servants. You could be trusted with little, so enter into the joy of the Creator. Come and share in even greater wealth.'

If the existing government of five hundred and forty-five lawmakers could think for the two hundred sixty millions of the rest of us, the United States' commitment to space development would be very different than it is now. It would consume much of the national budget and pay back the economy seven fold in newly created wealth. Be good stewards of the nation. At this moment, the key to unlock the door containing all these unbounded blessings lies in changing the Federal Republic to a National Democracy.

MESSAGES

MESSAGE TO CHRISTIANS

'I thought Christians were suppose to be meek and timid.'

A common derisive saying by non-Christians.

It's interesting that non-Christians repeat what they think they understand about the teachings of Jesus Christ to tell Christians who and what we are supposed to be. What non-Christians usually mean when they employ the phrase above is, 'Act fearful and powerless so I can squash you.'

Christians must immediately give up the sinful luxury of quarrelling with one another over foolish controversies about the laws of God. Leaders in pulpits high or low, must stop dividing the Body of Christ to gain market share. It's time to wake up and face the real danger that's at hand.

While Christians have argued with one another in defiance of Jesus Christ's commands, our Nation has been lost to the wolves in sheep's clothing. The wolves have so much power and Christians are so divided and weak from attacking one another that the facade is no longer necessary: The enemy has thrown off it's disguise.

If you have eyes to see, then look. If you have ears to hear then listen carefully. Nothing less than your life as a Christian and that of your children depend upon it. Your very life may depend upon what you decide to do with this information.

In the United States, and for Christians of a generation ago, it was easy to embrace the Federal Republic known as the United States of America. In the past, the citizens of our country whether they were Christians or not, almost universally practiced Christian principles.

Until recently, all our laws, whether you realized it or not, were in fact direct applications of Biblical laws and Jesus Christ's teachings. For Americans it was as if belief in the United States and their faith in God were one and the same.

It was understandable when you examine Jesus Christ's words. He was the originator of perfect freedom, brotherly love, forgiveness, equality, trust, thrift and a host of other essential beliefs and practices and social conditions without which Democracy can't exist. All the elements that must be present and are essential to the practice of Democracy are original and unique ideas of Jesus Christ. 'My command is this: Love each other as I have loved you. Greater love has no one than this, that he lay down his life for his friends. You are my friends if you do what I command. I no longer call you servants, because a servant does not know his master's business. Instead, I have called you friends, for everything I learned from my Father I have made known to you.... This is my command: Love each other.' (John 15:12-17) Egalitarianism for all humans regardless of class or social position was just one of the unique teachings of Jesus. If you read and study all the words of Jesus Christ you will understand the absolute dependency Democratic ideals have upon Christianity.

This book is a plan to establish a true Democracy in the United States for the first time. I've drawn the line between the Federal Republic and its five hundred and forty-five lawmakers who are sovereign over the Nation and where we the other two hundred sixty million citizens need to take our country. Now that the officials ruling the Federal Republic have thrown off their shroud and have exposed themselves as anti-Democracy and anti-Christian, where do we Christians stand?

We must become strong and united in the face of the maelstrom the anti-Christians have conjured up from their false teachings. This we can do but only if we are united. Jesus said, 'God did not give us a spirit of fear but of power, love and a sound mind.' We must embrace this spiritual truth to confront the enemy who is as Jesus compared to a 'lion roaming about seeking to devour you'.

Christians need to stop giving lip service to the notion that Christian history and principles should not be taught in public schools or practiced in government offices or business. It's too late for such dilettantism. The wolf has entered and rules the house. You are next in line to be eaten. North America may very well be populated by every race and nationality but in spite of the revisionist and cultural relativists, it is a historical fact that the United States Government was founded by Christians. Christians do not constitute the entire history of North America but Christianity certainly is the original foundation of Democratic principles of the government of the United States of America.

Americans need Christian principles in school if for no other reason than that quarreling children need to learn to respect and forgive one anther while they are still at the disagreement stage and before it erupts into physical violence, gun play, bloodshed and death. Forgiveness for those who wrong you is a unique Christian concept. Jesus Christ was the first person who ever lived to teach it.

Americans have seen the tragic reports from their own communities and other cities. The Nation is reaping in urban gangs, debt and other social catastrophes what has been sown by the five hundred and forty-five lawmakers for the last thirty years. Unless principles as taught by Jesus Christ are embraced wholesale at every level of Nation and by every leader, our Nation won't survive another thirty years as a place to live. I've described some of what will happen in the chapter on predictions.

I'm the first to admit it's extremely difficult to write about forgiveness while contemplating such a momentous change in government. Yet this is exactly what Jesus has commanded us to do. We need to change the government without bloodshed and without breaking the law. My personal goal is not to punish the five hundred and forty-five lawmakers currently in power but to peacefully and Constitutionally take sovereignty away from them and give it to 'we the people'.

The wisest and perhaps the kindest thing that American Christians can do for the five hundred and forty-five lawmakers and for ourselves is to deliver them from the temptation to sin by taking away their power. Replace them with wise legal advisors who make one political promise: Democracy. Like any addict the current group needs to get into treatment. If they are no longer given absolute power they can no longer be absolutely corrupt. If they want to keep their jobs, let them prove they are worthy by creating National Democracy immediately. Let them vote today to amend the Constitution as outlined in this book with out their usual conditions and trickery. They must prove their sincerity and devotion to the people of the Nation by immediate action. Words will no longer suffice. Tomorrow may be to late.

Only once in modern times has there been another world power that has changed governments without a full scale war: the Soviet Union. The news media makes an issue of the market economy the Russians are trying to establish because, with the media's anti-Christian agenda, it's all they understand. The Eastern European peoples, including the ethnic Russians, wanted more than anything was to be free from totalitarian rule to be able to practice Christianity. They understand, even if the Western news media won't admit it, that Eastern European societies and economies can only be built up with Christianity at the center. Anything else is tearing down. Seventy years of anti-Christian Soviet communist totalitarianism has shown everyone but those in the U.S. Democrat Party the utter folly of communism.

The solutions National Democracy will afford us will be perfectly eloquent but ruling ourselves will take some getting used to. Christians and non-Christians and even anti-Christians can agree upon the teaching of Christ which proclaims that the love of God described by Jesus can only be nurtured, not forced. Under National Democracy no one will be forced to be Christian although everyone will have to act in accordance with the civil laws which were all originally based upon Judeo-Christian principles. The difference is that after National Democracy the laws will be explained and enforced.

Under the current Federal Republic the symptoms of the systematic destruction of Christian principles are everywhere in our society. The ever-increasing numbers of lawsuits are a symptom of abandonment of Christianity as are the consequential failure of the government to offer any other alternatives to conflict resolution.

Christians play into the anti-Christian hand every time one of us proclaims that this or that group is a cult. I acknowledge that whole movements within Christianity are based upon division. But division is contrary to what Jesus taught. When it happens it is tragic. We are commanded to serve one another. Are we not at the same time all accountable directly to God? Did not Jesus say, 'The hand can't say to the eye I don't need you. Aren't all part of the same Body?' Elsewhere He said, 'I'm the vine you are the branches?' 'Judge not and you will not be judged.' 'Do not argue over foolish controversies about the law.' There are many such verses.

Growing up in the Roman Catholic Church, I can remember it was said about us that we worshiped statues and that the Mass in

Latin was really a secret language of Satan worship. (We were all taught Latin so we knew what was being said during the mass.) Since becoming an adult, I have been filled with the Holy Spirit of God. I understand even more. All Christians in this nation must stop such murmuring and slander against one another if we are to survive. Don't open your mouth to say that this or that Christian religion is a cult. Don't let others say it in your presence. After National Democracy is accomplished you can return to such 'admonishments' if you feel you must.

Jesus said, 'A house divided can't stand.' Likewise a nation divided cannot stand. Yet, this is what has been happening while Christians have hammered each other. The majority of the five hundred and forty-five lawmakers have used squabbling Christians as their example to further divide Americans because it's the best way for them to maintain control. They are dividing the Nation to take our attention off of the real and only issue which is that they, the elected representatives of the Federal Republic, are causing all of the Nation's problems deliberately to keep themselves in power. In spite of whatever lies they are telling Americans, their remaining in power depends upon the continuation of these problems and the end of democratic, Christian principles.

Whatever problems existed with the Branch Davidians in Waco, Texas, by the public's very acceptance of President Clinton's and the Justice Department's and the news media's labeling of them as a 'cult', the door was opened for the Federal Government to eradicate any Christians who are not politically correct.

I'm not defending David Koresh or any of his followers or his failures. I know nothing about them except what I've seen on television and read in the newspapers. But to whom were they a threat? Not to me certainly, nor you. I've read that until they were attacked they lead peaceful lives and were law-abiding, hard working citizens of their community of Waco, Texas. Even the government now admits that there was no sexual or other abuse of children there. Only the Federal Government Agents saw them as a threat. '*...the hour is coming when whoever kills you will think he is offering service to God. And they will do this because they have not known the Father, nor me.*' John 16.2 & 3.

Even if they were a threat, my point here is: Since when in the last thirty years have Christians been able to accept the news media's definition of who we are or what our motivations are? We are always reported as 'right wing extremists' or Nazis or homophobes. Christians are an easy target because we never hit back.

All my life I have heard individuals say that government can't legislate morality. I've considered this issue at length and I've come to this conclusion: Of course government can legislate morality. And in fact, when you understand that all our civil laws were originally based upon Judeo-Christian principles, legislating morality is the only legitimate and absolute function of government! In any event, whether you agree with my conclusion or not, once Americans have a National Democracy, the common sense of the majority will be able to confirm or deny each law.

According to the Bible as well as to history, God judges nations. We are stewards not only of our families, our businesses, but of our nation and beyond that this entire planet and even the Solar system. Christians must act together before those in control of our government succeed in totally eradicating the factual history of our Nation and then us soon after. You must wake up to the fact that it is true that those in government don't want us to be able to have thoughts apart from those which serve their own totalitarian agenda. 'Politically correct' thinking is nothing more than a form of whitewashing, or to put it more succinctly, brainwashing. The goal of those currently in power is to reach the point where everyone thinks the same socially engineered 'correct thoughts'. This came directly from the failed experiments with communism in Europe and Asia. This is the face of our current government. This is totalitarianism!

The majority of the five hundred and forty-five lawmakers' very successful move to change the Republic to a totalitarian government can't survive with a rational-thinking citizenry. That is why they are hell-bent upon denying the truth of Jesus Christ to the young. Only God grants reason and wisdom. Those who lack God's living Spirit in their lives have neither.

Unless we unite now with National Democracy as our one goal, I predict that more and more small Christian groups will be officially designated as cults by the government and attacked. And unfortunately the government will be aided and abetted by larger Christian groups who either won't want to get involved or who want to be rid of the smaller groups. (In the chapter titled 'Predictions For Christians' I describe what awaits after that.) These events will happen unless all Christians put aside all our differences and unite now. It's worth repeating: American Christians must put aside each and every difference and unite to become the leading force of change to insure that the Federal Republic becomes a National Democracy. This must happen immediately if we are going to have any future whatsoever in this country.

"If my people who are called by my name humble themselves and pray and seek my face and turn from their wicked ways then I will hear from heaven and will forgive their sin and heal their land."

2 Chronicles 7.14

Christians know, even if the rest of humanity doesn't, that everyone will one day stand before God and be made to give an accounting. Let it not be said of this generation of Christians that we were 'weighed in the balance and found wanting.'

MESSAGE TO NON-CHRISTIANS

Once the Constitution is amended and the Federal Republic is replaced by the National Democracy, the citizens will together find eloquent solutions for all the problems that have solutions. Until Democracy is realized, all Americans can unite upon the foundations of freedom. Let us not be divided. You have nothing to fear from Christians. The life Jesus described and His truth can only be nurtured with love. Christians don't take prisoners at gunpoint or drive around in gangs shooting total strangers.

Non-Christians may be very accurate in their assessments of men like Jim Bakker, Jim Swaggart and David Koresh yet miss the point of Jesus Christ's messages completely. You have to study Jesus's teachings for yourself to fully understand. Under National Democracy the only people who will be forced to do anything will be those who break the law. We will still have a President, Congress and Supreme Court but for the first time, each new law will be at least confirmed or denied by the majority of U.S. citizens, not just the existing five hundred and forty-five lawmakers in Washington D.C.

The majority of two hundred sixty million citizens of the United States of America have the right to peacefully change any aspect of the government at any time. It doesn't matter, for example, how many times House Speaker Thomas Foley, in coordination with the League of Women Voters, maintains that American citizens don't have the right to change the laws by setting such conditions as term limits. Our rights come not from the benevolence of the five hundred and forty-five lawmakers who rule over our government nor does it come from the Declaration of Independence, the Constitution and the Bill of Rights, although our rights are certainly recorded there. These rights come directly from God and are in fact part of human nature itself. Whether you believe in God or not, you need to realize that the government is not granting us our rights. You are conceived possessing them.

The words, 'Separation of Church and State' are not in the Constitution. The Supreme Court, lead by Justice Hugo Black, invented this principle and consequentially censored the factual teaching of United States history in the public schools.

Instead, today and under the guise of cultural relativism, any kind of unbalanced philosophy can and is now taught in the public schools of our Nation. In addition, children in some elementary schools are told to wear condoms, that suicidal same-sex practices are normal, chant mantras and that lesbian and homosexual parenting is desirable.

We are now into the second generation of young people who have passed through the public school system and who have been taught that there is no such thing as an absolute right or wrong. Millions of children of this second generation, fifteen and sixteen year olds, with no remorse have started warring on each other over trivialities. Thousands have become murderers in senseless killings.

This should alarm you but if it doesn't, have you ever considered why, in the last thirty years, Christianity has been singled out for removal from the schools and other institutions?

It is solely because we Christians alone know that our rights are from God. Those in government do not want you to know that. They want you to believe that all rights are granted by them. It follows then that if government grants us our rights, government can also take them away. This is exactly why the communist governments specifically forbid the practice of Christianity.

One of our basic freedoms is the freedom of speech which itself should guarantee the freedom to have access or be taught historically accurate information. Accurate knowledge of the history of the government of the United States, the history of Christians seeking freedom, has been deleted from public school's curriculum. This was accomplished by nine individuals of the Supreme Court who were elected by no one and cannot be removed from office unless the citizens change the government.

I recommend you join together with Christians to change the Federal Republic to a National Democracy before those in government succeed in completely taking away the rest of your freedoms.

MESSAGE FOR JEWS

To me, listening to President Clinton and the Justice Department blame David Koresh for bringing about his group's demise is like listening to recordings of Adolph Hitler and the Nazis blaming the Jews for bringing the Holocaust on themselves. It's also like reading how the Romans absolved themselves for the thousands of Jews who died on Masada. And this after the Romans destroyed Jerusalem, slaughtered tens of thousands and broke the nation.

I didn't understand nor am I advocating David Koresh's position. I only know what I've read in the newspaper and have seen on television. One thing is certain: Except for a handful of children and a few very old women, the Branch Davidians are dead. Who really knows what was said or done in the compound?

Perhaps Koresh said he was the Messiah on Earth or perhaps he didn't. Perhaps he molested children or perhaps he didn't. But these two reports were the only pieces of information that could be reported about Koresh that would make Christians and Jews alike turn away and say 'they deserved it'. David Koresh didn't represent Christianity and Christ's message necessarily any more than all poor and working class Caucasians are represented by KKK leader David Duke.

Those of us who believe in the living words of the Bible know that there can be no Kingdom of God without Jews. Jesus was a Jew. All the apostles were Jews. Jesus said we Gentiles were grafted into the vine and that if we failed to produce fruit in keeping with God's existing laws we would be cut out. Jesus said, 'I did not come to change the (Jewish) Law but to fulfill it.' The Bible is full of admonitions that the enemies of Israel are enemies of God. Jesus himself said, 'Salvation comes through the Jews.' Those of us who have been filled with what Jesus described as the 'Holy Spirt' know that God cannot be forced upon anyone but only nurtured by humans actually becoming and then acting out the perfect love of God. Spiritually, a person has to have freedom to choose or reject God or it all would be meaningless.

My point is that neither Jews nor any other minority group in America has anything to fear from a National Democracy of majority rule. In fact, freedom to be different, as long as you are not criminal or violent or a threat to public health, can only occur in a Nation who's laws are based upon Judeo-Christian values. The majority in government have labored to extinguish the knowledge of our heritage of true freedom which comes from God. That is exactly why freedom has eroded so severely and lawlessness has taken over in the last thirty years. This is what we must join together to stop.

PREDICTIONS

This book is about conclusions. In the last four decades, the leaders of the government of the United States of America have forced a transition. During my lifetime, the three branches of government have been deliberately lead away from Christian Democratic principles through a post-Christian period to where it is today. Our government is today purposefully anti-Christian and therefore anti-Democratic and guiding itself rapidly toward totalitarianism.

On March 8, 1948, Supreme Court Justice Hugo Black held that, 'both religion and the State can best work to achieve their lofty aims if each is left free from the other within its respective spheres'. (McCollum vs Board of Education) This was when the phrase, 'Separation of Church and State,' was first coined. In passing this ruling, the Supreme Court contradicted the historical reality that Democratic forms of government can only exist in and because of Christian values and in a society where the majority practice Christian principles.

On June 25, 1962, speaking for the Court, Justice Black held, 'that no government has the power to prescribe by law any particular form of prayer,' referring to public schools. While this idea in itself may have been worth a discussion by the majority of the citizens, they were never given a chance. The nine men just ordered it done. It opened the gate in the dam which caused the anti-Christian flood of lawlessness and abandonment of common sense that our Nation is drowning in today. If the citizens had been given the chance to vote to confirm or deny these two rulings, we would be living in a very different, peaceful and prosperous world today.

It's now been over three decades since the nine men in the Supreme Court took ideological control by edict over the public schools and imposed their own revisionist anti-Christian anti-Democracy history on American children. Because of nine lawyers, trained in situational ethics, the youth of the Nation have been denied nothing less than the history of their own ancestors, their Country and that of Western Civilization. They have not been freed but utterly abandoned.

Ethics, morality, love of truth, sanctity of life, individual freedom balanced with respect for authority and thrift are gone. Gone also are the principles of living in harmony with one's neighbors, and personal accountability and obligation to the Supreme Being. Virtually all the basic precepts of Democracy which are nothing less than the unique principles of Christianity were discarded as part and parcel of separating the Church from the State. All accomplished by a handful of profoundly confused but extremely powerful lawyers trained and corrupted by situational ethics.

At the same time, other practices and philosophies, no matter how distressed and deadly, have received nurturing and funding by the government through the Nation's public schools colleges and universities simply by calling themselves social movements, special interests or political support groups. I have stated elsewhere why the buyers and sellers in the market place of power have singled out Christianity for removal but disguised their attempts under the Separation of Church and State issue.

In the last twenty years, anti-Christian revisionist historians have outdone one another by portraying Christians as oppressors, terrorists and war mongers, when in truth, the only individual freedoms that exist here or anywhere on earth are because of Christians fashioning Jesus Christ's principles into the fabric of the law.

To save their own seats in government the majority of U.S. politicians and judges have caved into the, 'Christians are racist' mentality promoted especially by the tiny numbers but today extremely powerful anti-Christian Gay Rights advocates in government civil service, the news media and entertainment industry. In spite of the fact that Christians number in the hundreds of millions in the United States, we no longer are represented in any measure by the Federal Republic.

The rest of this chapter contains what I predict will happen next in our Nation if the two hundred sixty million Americans outside of national office fail to unite to change the United States government from a Federal Republic to a National Democracy. It is easy to predict what will happen next. A person only has to study the history of any time period on any continent to know what treatment Christians have received when the governments have turned against them as ours has done.

The legal foundation for this has already been laid in the existing anti-terrorist laws passed by congress specifically to persecute and imprison Christians involved in Operation Rescue. In January 1994 the Supreme Court ruled that Christians who demonstrate against abortions clinics can also be prosecuted and imprisoned under racketeering laws. In case you haven't noticed, Christians are now criminals by definition. The politicians will soon use or create an incident of international ramifications, probably a war or incident similar but on a larger scale to what was perpetrated in Waco, Texas to institute new even more restrictive laws regarding religion. These laws will be cleverly worded to cover all religions but in practice will apply only to Christians. They will be a series of decrees that will have as their theme, 'Peace or Religion'.

To save themselves and under pressure from the tiny but powerful special interests, the politicians will scramble for someone or something on which to affix the blame for the catastrophe. The Congress and President will pass more anti-religion acts one after another as terror under the guise of nationalism sweeps the country. At the same time the Second and Fourth Amendment rights will be further curtailed to the point where they will be in effect nullified.

It will be agreed by those in power that religion equals fanaticism. It will be axiomatic: If anyone disagrees with any facet of the new law they will be labeled a dangerous enemy of world peace. Christians who tell others the truth about Jesus will be considered guilty of hate crimes or terrorism.

To save and absolve themselves the Judges will agree with the new laws. Under the, 'Religion or Peace' decrees it won't be enough that public funds or facilities can't be used for religious purposes. In order to 'prevent' future wars, Christians will be singled out: Public support will no longer go to Christians in any measure. Christians will be barred from holding public office. They will not be permitted employment in Federal, State or Local government agencies.

Because homosexuals will be by that time be in command of the military, Christians will not be allowed to serve. Christians will be bared from teaching in public schools. Churches will lose tax exempt status. Since the airways are held in the public trust, Christians will be forbidden from working or appearing on television, radio or in films. Christians will be denied the right to vote unless they make a public declaration repudiating their beliefs. In time, they will not be able to own property. No one will be allowed to buy or sell anything unless they accept a computer chip implanted either in their foreheads or on their right hand which will store personal information. The chip will be scanned by remote computer at all times. (This technology already exists and is currently being used experimentally on dogs.)

By virtually outlawing what had once had been the foundation of democracy, the politicians and a hysterical government will reason there will never be another war. The Christian Churches that aren't burned down by arsonists will be put to the torch by local fire departments under police supervision as a lesson to the other Christian 'fanatics'. Millions of Christians will protest openly and thus will 'prove' their violent nature and intent. But by that time it will be too late for actions to be of any good.

Tens of millions will be sent to concentration camps and their children will be handed over to the State for deprogramming. Millions will then be executed or simply murdered. The anti-Christians in government will be besotted on the blood of the faithful. The social and economic cost to those who remain faithful will be absolute.

Those Christians who can will flee the country but for most it will be too late. Then the Nation will cease to exist as the anti-Christians destroy one another or are destroyed utterly by an outside force.

'Fallen! Fallen is Babylon the Great!
She has become a home for demons
and a haunt for every evil spirit.
a perch for every unclean and
carnivorous bird.
For all the nations have drunk
the maddening wine of her
adulteries.
The rulers of the earth committed
adultery with her,
and the merchants of the earth grew
rich from her excessive luxuries.
Therefore in one day her plagues will over take her:
death, mourning and famine.
She will be consumed by fire,
for mighty is the Lord God who

judges her.
When the rulers of the earth who
committed adultery with her and shared
her luxury see the smoke of her burning,
they will weep and mourn over her.
Terrified at her torment they will
stand far off and cry:
'Woe! Woe, O great city,'
O Babylon, city of power!
In one hour your doom has come!'

Condensed from Revelation 18

The continent of North America will be a virtual wasteland inhabited by people, living in scatted pockets. They will have to scrounge among the ruins just to exist. They will know and remember little or nothing about us, God, or our once great Nation. These events and others too horrifying to describe are just ahead for everyone if we fail to act now to change the Federal Republic to a National Democracy.

WHAT IS
TO BE DONE?

*'And you will know the truth
and the truth will set you free.'*

Jesus Christ

As recorded in the book of John 8:32

I was once told that there is a old and very private joke in Washington D.C. among the senior leaders of the five hundred and forty-five lawmakers who rule our nation. It is dusted off and retold whenever an issue is forced upon the government by the citizens themselves.

It goes something like this: After watching an event such as Ronald Reagan's landslide re-election in 1984 on television the Speaker of the House of Representatives turns to the Senate Majority Leader and mutters, 'For a while, I thought they (the citizens) were actually going to do something.'

The joke is on us. The majority of federal republicans in office don't care what the U.S. citizens think as long as the rest of the two hundred sixty million Americans don't do anything about it. Ross Perot's idea for an electronic town hall is just another public opinion poll and the politicians wouldn't be legally bound to honor it any more than they are any poll now.

From now and until the moment the Constitution is amended and National Democracy is realized the only issue that matters is Democracy. All other issues are nothing more than symptoms of the lack of citizen sovereignty. Americans must stop allowing ourselves to be divided by the five hundred and forty-five lawmakers and their tax supported legions. We must take it upon ourselves to peacefully change the Federal Republic to a National Democracy by electing new leaders committed to one goal. The citizens must become sovereign over the three branches of government as proposed in this book. Exactly the opposite of now. A few hundred people must no longer be sovereign over hundreds of millions.

Americans must empower themselves to be able to vote, item by item, for or against every law, tax, policy, treaty, constitutional question and everything else that effects us before such items become the law of the land. Only changing the Republic to a Democracy will give us this ability.

Any political parties or candidates for office that promote any other issue must be passed over until Democracy is realized. After Democracy, the majority of voters will pass judgment and create every law and every policy. Everything.

Americans must stop blaming each other, stop accepting the false and divisive solutions the five hundred and forty-five lawyers are offering us and take action.

We must stop trying to identify with the tiny number of Democrats or Republicans in power. Stop cooperating with the divisiveness of pro-Republic personalities like Bill Clinton, Thomas Foley or Ross Perot. We must start identifying with other Americans. Democracy is the one and only movement that can unify America and end the manufactured problems created by those now in power. Christians must put aside the desire to admonish, rebuke, correct or criticize one another for any reason at least until Democracy is realized. The new focus should be simply called, 'National Democracy'.

In order to create Democracy, the citizens will have to take over and replace all but a handful of the current anti-Democracy candidates in the existing three major parties with new pro-Democracy citizens. All Americans can agree on one issue until Democracy is realized. After that, every issue will be sorted out item by item in general elections. It may not be necessary to create a new political party but that option is not ruled out.

For you the future senators, congressmen, presidents, governors, mayors and school board members of the National Democracy, I offer congratulations in advance. Only you, the Americans, can guarantee that the next President will be the last President of the Federal Republic and the first President of the National Democracy.

The American Federal Republic was a Christian Nation until just over three decades ago. It was the land of the free and the home of the brave. It will be extremely difficult at first but sooner than later the current five hundred and forty-five lawmakers will capitulate. The pro-Republic, anti-Democracy forces may fight to the death to prevent change. I pray that they accept the wisdom of peaceful change just as did their counterparts in government in the ex-Soviet Union. But expect to witness any and all types of persecutions against pro-Democracy advocates as Democracy advances. Expect any kind of 'pravda' against Democracy to come from the mouths of those currently in government. If Americans stick to the Democracy amendments outlined in this book the voters can then decide every other issue item by item. The National Democracy of the United States of American will be a nation of true freedom for all individuals for the first time. America will be the land of the free and the home of the brave reborn.

As you read this you may be asking yourself if you have the qualifications or even the desire to be a national office holder. I know many women and men in the productive sector who are more than qualified but who don't want to get into the gutter with the current batch of lawyers in power. Today what matters more than anything is that you want National Democracy and that you are willing to abide by the nation's existing laws, by amending the Constitution to obtain one. You must be dedicated to peacefully yielding sovereignty to American citizens.

It may be true that you've never held a political office like Bill Clinton or Thomas Foley. But you've held something of far greater importance than either of them have ever experienced. You've held a job.

John Wayne, was often quoted as having said, *'A man's got to do what a man's got to do.'* His words and his memory are today vilified by the anti-Democracy forces in our country for a variety of facile reasons. But every man and women with common sense understands what the phrase means and that it applies to the entire human condition at one time or another. This is such a time. You cannot have a Democracy without taking deliberate action. And if you choose to do nothing and allow the federal republicans and the Federal Republic to continue as it is you will very soon live in a nation that you do not recognize as home.

The Twenty-First Century will itself usher in the Third Millennium. If Americans can unite under the cause of Democracy, the age will begin with a new enlightenment. You will be the Founders of National Democracy, the people future generations look back to thank for their freedom.

As Leo Thorsness said, 'Freedom equals responsibility.' Change won't be without mistakes or hard work and danger. But at least the mistakes will be yours and you will have the power to speedily correct them. You won't have to pay for the avaricious blunders of the five hundred and forty-five lawmakers currently in power any longer.

Now that you've read it, you know that this book is more than a plan for Democracy. It is in fact a Declaration of Freedom.

'And for the support of this declaration,
with a firm Reliance on the
Protection of divine Providence,
we mutually pledge to each other our lives,
our Fortunes and our sacred Honor.'

From the Declaration of Independence.

Now that Democracy is possible, it is inevitable.

God bless you.

Index

Index

Index

Index

Index

Index

Index

Democracy For Americans

Talk About Writing! ™

Talk live one on one with writer/publisher

Vincent Mountjoy-Pepka

(Founder of Kick Press, Inc.)

not in Service

☎ 900-678-0321

$3.99 per minute. Average call costs $24 (for six minutes).

Callers must be 18 years or older.
Touch tone phone required.

Vincent is generally available to talk Monday
through Friday 10 A.M. to 6 P.M. Pacific time zone.

Customer service # (206) 884-5085

✉ Kick Press, Inc. P.O. Box 112 Vaughn, Washington 98394.

*No charge to call
me at this number
V.M-P*

Democracy For Americans

Democracy For Americans

Democracy For Americans

Order Now By Calling Toll Free

Additional copies of **Democracy For Americans** can be ordered from any book store or you can order directly by telephone from Lifeline Resources (a division of Inspirit, Inc.) Mail orders are handled directly by Kick Press, Inc.

Price per copy: $12.00 U.S. $18.00 Canada

☎
Telephone orders:

for ordering only
Call Toll Free: 1-800-272-1225.
Have your Visa or MasterCard ready.

Card Number: _____

Name On Card: _____

Exp. date:_____ / _____

✉
Postal orders:

make payment to:
Kick Press, Inc.
P.O. Box 112
Vaughn, Washington 98394

☞
Handling and Shipping:

For **all** orders please add $ 2.00 for the first book and 75 cents for each additional book shipped to the same mailing address. (For Express Mail add $ 3.00 per book)

❽
Sales Tax:

Please add an additional 8.2% to the total for books shipped to Washington State residences.

$
Acceptable Payment:

Check or Money Order
Visa, MasterCard.

Most orders will be shipped within a 48-hour period. (Surface shipping may occasionally take several weeks.)

Democracy For Americans